Trails of Evidence:
How Forensic Science Works

Elizabeth A. Murray, Ph.D.

THE
GREAT
COURSES®

PUBLISHED BY:

THE GREAT COURSES
Corporate Headquarters
4840 Westfields Boulevard, Suite 500
Chantilly, Virginia 20151-2299
Phone: 1-800-832-2412
Fax: 703-378-3819
www.thegreatcourses.com

Elizabeth A. Murray, Ph.D., D-ABFA
Professor of Biology
and Forensic Anthropologist
College of Mount St. Joseph

Professor Elizabeth A. Murray is a forensic anthropologist who is also Professor of Biology at the College of Mount St. Joseph, where she teaches doctoral-level cadaver-based human gross anatomy and undergraduate-level vertebrate anatomy and physiology, musculoskeletal anatomy, and forensic science. She received her bachelor's degree in Biology from the College of Mount St. Joseph, and she received her master's degree in Anthropology and her doctoral degree in Interdisciplinary Studies in Human Biology from the University of Cincinnati.

Dr. Murray is an award-winning teacher who has received the Sears-Roebuck Foundation Teaching Excellence and Campus Leadership Award and who has twice earned the Sister Adele Clifford Excellence in Teaching Award. She has also served as an instructor for numerous professional organizations, including the U.S. Department of Justice/National Institute of Justice's National Missing and Unidentified Persons System (NamUs) training academy, the American Academy of Forensic Sciences (AAFS) Student Academy, the Armed Forces Institute of Pathology, the Wayne State University School of Medicine's Medicolegal Investigation of Death program, and the International Association of Coroners & Medical Examiners.

Most of Dr. Murray's regular forensic casework has been in Ohio and Kentucky, where she has participated in hundreds of forensic investigations involving skeletal, decomposing, burned, buried, and dismembered human remains. A Fellow of the AAFS, she is 1 of fewer than 100 anthropologists who are certified as a Diplomate by the American Board of Forensic Anthropology. Dr. Murray is a member of the Forensic Services Team for NamUs and is the Forensic Anthropology Consultant on the National

Advisory Board for Parents of Murdered Children. She is also on the Mass Disaster Team for the Cincinnati/Northern Kentucky International Airport.

In 1994, Dr. Murray was recruited by the Armed Forces Institute of Pathology to participate in morgue operations after the crash of American Eagle Flight 4184 in Roselawn, Indiana. She also served as a visiting scientist to the U.S. Army Central Identification Laboratory, for which she led a team of military personnel in the recovery of a Vietnam War–era plane crash site in the jungle of Laos. As a consultant and on-screen personality for the National Geographic Channel's *Skeleton Crew* (aired internationally as *Buried Secrets*), Dr. Murray was dispatched to observe and participate in fieldwork with the Guatemalan Forensic Anthropology Foundation. This 4-part miniseries showcased the uses of forensic anthropology in analyzing historical mysteries and modern forensic contexts. In addition, Dr. Murray served as a regular cast member on the Discovery Fit & Health series *Skeleton Stories* and has appeared on such television shows as *America's Most Wanted*, *The New Detectives*, and *Forensic Files*.

Dr. Murray's publications include numerous entries in the *Proceedings*, published by the AAFS, as well as books and chapters covering both historical and forensic anthropological analyses. Dr. Murray's book *Death: Corpses, Cadavers, and Other Grave Matters* was named 1 of the 2011 top 10 summer reads for students by the American Association for the Advancement of Science. Her second book in this series focuses on the uses of forensic science in human identification and is scheduled for publication in 2012. ∎

Table of Contents

Table of Contents

Table of Contents

SUPPLEMENTAL MATERIAL

Trails of Evidence: How Forensic Science Works

Scope:

Although forensic science has become an extremely popular and pervasive subject in television programs, films, and literature, many members of the general public have only a limited understanding of the science behind forensic evidence and investigations. This course introduces the multidisciplinary field of forensic science, using real casework to illustrate basic principles.

This course begins with an overview of forensic science in the public eye and then briefly covers evidence and crime-scene investigation. Then, the course launches into a series of lectures that cover specific topics, including fingerprints, firearms, shoe prints, textile fibers, hair, plant and animal evidence, and body fluid analysis. Each lecture reviews how particular types of evidence are collected or documented at the scene and how laboratories analyze evidence and make comparisons. As the course progresses, more complex issues are introduced, such as DNA analysis, toxicology, and the various ways in which substance abuse impacts forensic science. When needed, underlying biological and chemical principles will be reviewed to help you understand the basics behind these forensic specialties.

Next, the discussion turns to the forensic analysis of questioned documents, such as forgeries, and then to increasingly more high-tech crimes, including computer forensics and other forms of digital evidence. This leads into lectures about other engineering applications, such as the forensic analyses of structural failures and building collapses, including the destruction of the World Trade Center's twin towers during the terrorist attacks of September 11, 2001. Additional lectures explore the analysis of vehicular accident reconstruction, arson, and bombing investigations. Physical science underlies the way blood is distributed at crime and accident scenes during bodily trauma, so forensic bloodstain pattern analysis will also be addressed.

Because many of the most serious forensic investigations involve the loss of human life, a lecture on the science of death leads into a discussion of death investigation in a variety of contexts. Forensic pathology and the autopsy process are introduced in addition to the ways in which investigators estimate the timing of death. Topics related to advanced decomposition explain how insects and other environmental factors destroy soft tissues and turn bodies into skeletons. Then, you will learn the basics of forensic anthropology and how bones assist in death investigations. Forensic dentistry is used to help identify unknown persons, and odontologists examine bite marks on both living and dead victims. Forensic art also involves both the living and the dead—such as when police sketch artists attempt to re-create the appearance of a suspect or when a facial reproduction is created from a skull. Real casework continues to be used to illustrate numerous principles in this part of the course.

The behavioral sciences play a major role in criminal investigations, so the next few lectures focus on the psychological aspects of forensic science. Interview, interrogation, and intelligence gathering are discussed—as well as criminal profiling and an examination of motive—using actual cases. You'll also discover how effective, or ineffective, memory is within criminal investigations through an exploration of eyewitness testimony. Forensic psychology and psychiatry play roles in the legal system—in determining issues of competency and sanity, for example—and this leads the course into a series of lectures that focus on the intersection of forensic science and the courtroom. The nature of evidence and how it is prepared for and presented at trial are discussed in regards to both civil and criminal matters. The roles of expert witnesses are examined, including rules that govern their testimony in court. In addition, career paths that lead to expertise in forensic science are briefly discussed.

Toward the end of the course, the topic of crime will be approached from a general perspective, but a few lectures will also address specific crimes in which certain pieces of forensic evidence were key. Cases deal with drunk driving, identity theft, kidnapping, arson, and murder and address both historic and modern issues involving some famous and notorious perpetrators. To showcase some interdisciplinary uses of what you have learned in the course, the final 2 lectures cover how forensic science is used in mass-disaster settings and the ways in which various forensic science disciplines intersect to identify unknown persons.

Each lecture in this course typically presents some of the basic theory behind one or more forensic techniques along with some historical background to put current methods into context. This course is intended to introduce you to the breadth of scientific disciplines used in legal contexts by taking you on a number of journeys—from the crime scene to the courtroom. Along the way, this course will help debunk some of the Hollywood hype by illustrating how forensic science is really used in the detection and resolution of criminal activity.

Using Science—Crime Scene to Courtroom
Lecture 1

In the past 10 to 15 years, the popularity of forensic science—especially as portrayed in books, television shows, and movies—has exploded. This course examines real forensic casework and the technology, science, and sleuthing that is used to unravel it. During your journey through this course, you will learn that forensic science is interdisciplinary, and a single problem is often approached from multiple directions. You will also learn about the many ways that science is used in the pursuit of justice so that you can bust the myths that Hollywood has created.

What Is Forensic Science?
- The most common misconception about forensic science is that it is mostly about criminal activity that leads to death. In fact, the word "forensic" comes from the Latin word for "public," which is "forum." Therefore, something that is forensic is open to public debate or for public interpretation.

- Because the legal system is founded on debate and argument, forensic science involves using science to inform legal matters—including both criminal and civil issues. However, while legal systems may differ in what is or is not considered criminal activity throughout the world, what constitutes good science does not vary.

- Good science is universal because it is a process. Science is a search for information that helps us learn about and explain our world; it isn't just a bunch of facts that are static.

The Scientific Method
- The first step in the scientific method is to make an observation about something—such as a plant growing well in a certain part of your garden.

- The next step is to generate a hypothesis, which is your initial attempt to explain your observation.

- Then, to test your hypothesis, you have to do experiments and collect data. This step in the scientific method might be simple, or it could become complex, depending on the nature of the issue.

- Finally, you have to analyze the results of your experiments and compare them to your original hypothesis.

- If the conclusions from your experiment matches up to your hypothesis, then you might have discovered the best explanation for the issue you were trying to understand. On the other hand, if your experiments don't support your hypothesis, you need to throw out your original hypothesis and come up with another explanation for your issue.

The Human Element of Forensic Science
- In general, human beings are curious, and we're also pretty good problem solvers. Every day—in restaurants, airports, and grocery stores—we make observations and invent explanations for them. Some of these hypotheses are testable while others are not much more than sheer speculation.

- In order to become a forensic scientist, you have to first be a scientist. Forensic scientists make observations, but those observations are related to things that are possibly of legal importance. Those initial observations may end up being parts of a crime scene or criminal investigation.

- Forensic scientists, investigators, and analysts have to come up with logical and reasonable explanations for what they observe, and if they hold true to science, those hypotheses should be neutral statements—not accusatory ones.

- In order to show whether their hypotheses are sound, forensic scientists—like all other scientists—have to ask questions and collect data. If the results of their tests disagree with their original hunches, then regardless of what they would like to believe, honest and competent forensic scientists have to abandon their initial direction and come up with another plausible explanation for what happened. Then, that secondary hunch has to be tested and analyzed.

Evidence technicians are trained in how to pick up a loaded gun versus how to collect a spilled liquid.

- If we are to trust in any form of science, we have to believe that the people who are observing, testing, analyzing results, and interpreting data are as objective as possible. Human beings have biases, but good investigators and scientists need to do everything they can to leave those biases behind when they enter the crime scene, laboratory, or courtroom.

- However, there's a big difference between hypotheses and theories that are based on training and prior experience and those that are based on unfounded, preconceived, or ill-conceived notions.

Forensic Science and the Law

- Forensic science is not the same as criminology, which is a sociological study of crime, criminals, and victims. A person might enter criminology through the behavioral sciences to study the sociology and psychology behind criminal behavior.

- Forensic science is also not the same as criminal justice. Graduates from criminal justice programs typically work in law enforcement—not in forensic labs.

- The best preparation for forensic science is a broad-based background that combines biology, chemistry, and physics. Law enforcement officers are heavily involved in crime-scene investigations because they assemble the pieces of crimes, but the bulk of the analysis of physical crime-scene evidence falls on scientists. As technology has advanced the field, a strong foundation in lab sciences is the basis for today's forensic careers.

- Science as a mechanism for understanding the world around us is not only international, but it is also universal. However, what's viewed as legal or illegal behavior is linked to a person's culture. Legal systems and laws vary around the world, and they change over time as cultures evolve and exchange ideas.

- The focus of this course is not to study crime, criminals, or legal systems. Instead, this course focuses on how science is applied in legal settings and addresses how evidence is gathered, tested, and considered—regardless of what a given culture considers right or wrong.

The Start of the Forensic Craze

- The infamous trial of the American football star O. J. Simpson was a highly publicized and televised 9-month ordeal, and it was the beginning of the forensic science explosion that began in the United States. During the many months of testimony, several forensic scientists took the stand and spoke not only to the judge, jury, and packed courtroom, but also to a riveted public, who suddenly were fascinated with science and how it could be used—and possibly abused—in order to demonstrate guilt or innocence.

- Regardless of how you feel about the outcome of the trial, nobody can question the impact it had upon the public perception and general awareness of the field of forensic science. From the evidence presented—including hair analysis, autopsy results, bloody socks, carpet fibers, prior offenses, and DNA profiling—the public learned that there are many different specialties and experts involved in forensics and that the legal system has rules that govern the presentation of both facts and opinions at trial.

From Professor Murray's Forensic Files

One morning, in a nature preserve just outside of a town in southwestern Ohio, a man was walking his dog and discovered a human skull almost hidden by some tall grass. The skull was taken to the Montgomery County Court's office in Dayton, Ohio, and I was called in.

After examining the skull and taking measurements, I guessed that the skull was most likely from a white female who was young to middle aged. The skull didn't have any flesh on it, but I knew it was recent because there was still a decomposition odor. Police searched the area, but they didn't find anything else. At the morgue, they took a tooth from the skull for DNA analysis.

In the meantime, based on the physical description that I had given, the police began to go through local missing persons reports and discovered that several months earlier, a woman reported her daughter Shannon missing in that same general area. When the DNA results from the skull came back from the lab, they were compared to a reference sample the mother provided, and the skull was identified as Shannon's.

Several months later, a park ranger was driving his rounds one night in a nature area in southwestern Ohio. As he turned a bend in the road, a naked woman came running out of the woods screaming, "He's trying to kill me!" The police surrounded the area and closed in on a man who was trying to make his way through the woods.

The terrified woman told police that she had willingly gone with this man to provide sex for money and that he had attempted to strangle her. Somehow, she managed to get free, and then she was discovered by the park ranger.

After the police captured the man, they searched his car and found what appeared to be blood in the trunk. Investigators developed a DNA profile from that dried blood, and it matched Shannon's profile. As a result, not only was he charged with the attempted murder of the lady in the park, he was also charged with Shannon's murder.

When the news of this attempted murder was released to the public, a handful of other women started to come forward to tell their own horrendous stories of their encounters with this man.

When it came time for the trial, one of the problems was that many of these women were drug addicts—and they were all known prostitutes—and every time they were called into the police station for a pretrial conference, they would either be high or agitated. Because these women would probably not make very good witnesses, the county prosecutor decided to offer the murderer a plea bargain if he would lead us to the rest of Shannon's remains—over 18 months after her skull was found.

The man led police to the location of the rest of her body: the backyard of his rural house, where he lived with his wife and 2 children. When asked where he buried Shannon, the man pointed to a long stretch of fencing that encompassed the cornfields behind his house. He wasn't sure of the exact location.

Then, it was my job to locate and exhume the unmarked grave where allegedly we would find the rest of Shannon's remains. I got down on my hands and knees and started to crawl slowly along the fence. I knew that the soil above Shannon's body could not have been put back exactly the way it was before he buried her.

Suddenly, I hit about a 6-foot stretch along the fence that was bumpy. This observation led to the hypothesis that Shannon was buried here, so we pulled up the grass with our hands and started to dig with shovels. Eventually, we hit something: an exposed edge of bone that was about the size of my pinkie finger that turned out to be Shannon's left iliac crest, which is the front edge of the hipbone.

Within the following few hours, I removed Shannon's remains from the man's backyard, and after almost 2 years, we were able to reunite Shannon's skull with the rest of her bones so that her family could give her a proper burial.

Questions to Consider

1.   What does the term "forensic" mean?

2.   How do you know what you know about forensic science?

3.   What are some of the events responsible for the current public interest in forensic science?

4.   What do you hope to gain from this course?

Crime Scenes and Forensic Evidence
Lecture 2

Although there are rules of conduct and punishments for inappropriate behavior in many other groups of social animals, human beings are unique in terms of formalizing codes of conduct into laws and attempting to use logic and the scientific method to identify the unknown elements of crimes. Forensic science involves much more than forming logical conclusions. It involves analyzing specific pieces of evidence and systematically asking probative questions of the people involved—including victims, witnesses, and even potential criminals.

Crime-scene Investigation

- One of the most famous guiding scientific theorems of criminal investigation is known as Locard's exchange principle. Edmond Locard was a French forensic scientist who, about a century ago, set forth the idea that nobody can commit a crime without leaving something behind or altering the surroundings—even if the changes are imperceptible.

- As we interact with our environment and move through space and time, we always leave a trail. That trail might be made up of minute amounts of material known as trace evidence, or someone can generate a mountain of evidence. How much time 2 things spend in contact with one another is one of the main factors behind how much evidence is exchanged.

- In any crime-scene investigation, there are issues regarding the treatment of injured victims and the safety of first responders. These are critical factors in the initial response of law enforcement and emergency workers, who will always attend to lifesaving measures first—if they can.

- Sometimes, unfortunately, the initial assessment of the crime scene can damage or even destroy important evidence. However, if lives can be saved in a situation, any damage to evidence is considered an acceptable loss.

- Law enforcement officers also have to quickly figure out whether the person who committed the crime might still be on the scene—not only for their own safety, but also because there's the possibility of a quick capture.

- There can also be dangerous chemicals or disease-causing microorganisms left behind at certain crime scenes. Clandestine methamphetamine labs are notorious for the amount of toxic and combustible chemicals they generate and sometimes store.

- Some crime scenes are called hot zones when major biohazards are present—such as anthrax, nerve gas, or any other biological, chemical, radiological, or nuclear threat. These scenes can be accidental, can come from natural disasters, or can relate to crimes, such as bioterrorism.

- First responders and law enforcement investigators have to be trained in how to approach and search these types of dangerous scenes, and they need the right personal protective gear to recover victims, gather evidence, and analyze what might have happened.

- Another immediate consideration has to be containing and securing the scene and limiting access to only people with a good reason to be there. Somebody has to maintain a careful log of everyone who enters and exits a crime scene—and at precisely what time.

- Anyone at the scene becomes a potential witness at a future trial. Therefore, news reporters, curious bystanders, distraught family members, and even potential looters have to be controlled. Any of those people can jeopardize the crime scene—not only by their physical presence, but also through the information they could gather that might thwart the investigation. Unnecessary people at a crime scene can introduce additional fingerprints, footprints, tire tracks, hair, and DNA.

- Public access also has to be controlled. Media reports with specific information have the potential to tip off a suspect or reveal details that might be better kept for use by law enforcement during the questioning of any victims, witnesses, or suspects.

- Even the investigators can jeopardize evidence, so they need to have a specific search strategy for a given crime scene that will minimize their impact while maximizing the evidence they gather. Additionally, before any active search is undertaken, the appropriate legal standards for search and seizure must be met.

Identifying and Documenting Evidence

- The minute they step onto the scene of a crime, investigators have to consider everything they see around them as potential evidence. Using the context between and among objects—and the normal and abnormal relationships between things—they have to figure out what might be evidence and how it may be linked to other things they see.

- At a crime scene, there are going to be some assumptions made before any formal scientific testing. There are some tests, known as field tests, that can allow for some initial screening in the field, such as on blood or illegal drugs.

- Things of potential value to an investigation vary not only in their ability to immediately spot them, but also in their ability to preserve them for possible collection and analysis. Documentation is extremely important at the scene.

- Blood spatter, for example, is an example of pattern evidence. In order to reconstruct the history of what happened at a bloody scene, it's the pattern the blood makes on surfaces it hits that is the key to a full understanding of the scene. Photography and a careful map of the scene are crucial.

- Years can pass between when a crime occurs and when it may come before a judge and jury, and while bullets, hairs, and fibers can be picked up and preserved fairly indefinitely, some types of pattern evidence are transient and can basically only be preserved with images.

- As an alternative to photography, hand-drawn sketches and maps can be used to preserve a scene. These sketches don't have to be drawn to scale, but the idea is to map and measure the relationships between important objects at a scene. If possible, all the points on the sketch should be measured from a single fixed and permanent point called a datum, which can be anything reasonably permanent—such as the corner of a building.

- Today's state-of-the-art methods for documenting scenes include digital photography, video photography, and even portable electronic computerized mapping systems known as total station survey systems. This documentation might occur long before suspected evidence is confidently known to be a particular substance or especially long before that substance can be attributed to a particular individual.

- A potential crime scene has to be thoroughly documented not only photographically, but also by carefully written notes. Initially, you might not know the evidentiary value of a specific item. That's the reason crime-scene investigation requires keen observational skills, a methodical approach, good logic, and the willingness to being fairly compulsive about documentation.

Searching and Analyzing Crime Scenes
- Because each situation and scene is unique, different strategies have to be considered before collecting any potential evidence at a crime scene. Crime-scene analysts should do some careful planning before launching into a crime scene because evidence could be lost if they don't.

- There are a few standard patterns that are used to search scenes: Grid patterns, circular patterns, and line patterns are probably the most common.

- Searching and analyzing a crime scene is a complicated and destructive process, and any damage that is done can derail an investigation and can even make evidence unacceptable in a court of law.

- Crime-scene analysts are also subject to Locard's exchange principle. As they move through a scene to document and collect evidence, they only get one chance to view the area in the exact way in which they found it. Every item they move or pick up changes the scene forever.

- Television shows make searching a room look so easy: Actors just blunder in and start picking stuff up. Most likely, there are crime scenes where investigators have done that, but a good scene investigator puts a lot of effort into solving a crime and making sure that the proper legal conditions are maintained.

- Good communication between people who are—or may need to be—involved in the scene search is critical in the initial stages of

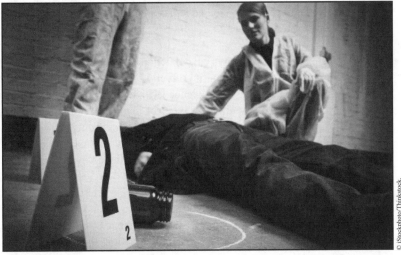

© iStockphoto/Thinkstock.

Interactions between people and things change the environment and leave clues to follow at a crime scene.

an investigation. This ranges from bringing in the medical examiner or coroner if a death is involved to making sure there is permission to search from the legal authorities. Additionally, someone has to do the mundane task of making sure that plenty of the right kind of supplies are available to gather evidence.

- Even the everyday language among the officers and investigators at the scene is important. Any type of inconsistency has the potential to complicate things in the future—especially when it comes to presenting evidence at trial.

- Another critical issue in crime-scene analysis is known as chain of custody. As soon as something is collected as evidence, the chain of custody for that item has to be maintained as a physical log of who handled the evidence, for how long they had it, and where they kept it while it was in their possession. Without a good chain of custody, critical evidence might not make it to trial.

- A good evidence custodian is critical to a forensic investigation. This person takes charge of evidence, logs it in, and makes sure that everything is properly labeled and sealed with evidence tape before it leaves the scene.

- When it comes to the physical collection of evidence—picking it up, handling it, and preserving it correctly—each type of evidence has its own specific needs, so evidence technicians have to be trained on how to collect many different types of items and substances. They also have to be sure to take known standards from the scene that might be used in future comparisons. Many forensic lab analyses involve comparing known evidence to questioned-evidence.

General Guidelines for Evidence
- Physical evidence varies in permanence, so a quick decision might need to be made when an investigator enters a scene. Crime-scene personnel have to quickly assess the situation and prioritize their actions.

- Evidence can be a direct transfer from one source to another, or it can have one or more intermediary transfers between its initial source and where it is eventually found—called an indirect transfer.

- Evidence can be classified in various ways. Recognizing that something belongs to a particular group is general and obvious, such as identifying something as hair, but further defining an item as part of a group of similar items with similar features—such as identifying the hair as cat hair—is called class identification. The most distinctive type of evidence identification puts an item into a group by itself, called individualizing identification.

- Not all evidence can be sampled, and not all of it can be tested. Crime-scene technicians need protocols for how much evidence to collect, and labs need protocols for how much to test to ensure that representative sampling and testing take place.

- Evidence typically consists of both physical objects and intangible evidence such as testimony. Technological advances have added other types of evidence that don't have a physical presence.

Questions to Consider

1. By whom and how are crime scenes discovered?

2. What are the initial responsibilities of law enforcement at a crime scene?

3. What is Locard's exchange principle?

4. What is the difference between known and unknown types of evidence?

5. What is the difference between class evidence and individuating evidence?

6. Can all evidence be collected at a crime scene?

Fingerprint Science—Hands-Down ID
Lecture 3

Fingerprints are one of the oldest and still most commonly used types of forensic evidence. Fingerprints are evidence of our presence that we leave on objects within our environment. Some of those fingerprints are nearly immediately erased or smeared over by the next person that comes in contact with the same object, but other prints might linger indefinitely. Even though it has been around for a long time, fingerprint science still holds new potential in solving crimes—sometimes even after a long time has elapsed.

The History of Fingerprinting

- Fingerprints have provided major evidence in countless criminal investigations, and their validity has long been widely accepted as proof of a person's identity.

- In the 1860s, William Hershel, who was a British official in colonial India, was using handprints of the Indian people he dealt with as a form of signature on contracts. Out of interest, Hershel tracked his own fingerprints for over 50 years, establishing that the patterns of fingerprints do not change over a lifetime.

- Henry Faulds is sometimes credited with the first true forensic application of fingerprints when he helped Tokyo police investigate a burglary in the 1880s. Faulds also tried to chemically alter his own prints and noticed that they grew back.

- Expanding on the work of Faulds, Sir Francis Galton—Charles Darwin's cousin—recognized that fingerprint patterns don't change as we age and that all prints can be essentially grouped into 3 main classifications: arches, loops, and whorls. Galton also did some statistical work on the probability of 2 people having the same prints, which basically established that fingerprints are unique. In fact, no 2 people have the same prints—not even identical twins.

Skin and Fingerprints

- The skin on vertebrate animals—including fish, amphibians, reptiles, birds, and mammals—has 2 main layers: an outer layer called the epidermis and a deeper layer known as the dermis. The epidermis is made of tightly packed cells that form a barrier to the outside world, and the dermis underneath has blood vessels, different kinds of glands, and other structures—such as scales, feathers, hairs, or nails—anchored in it.

- All surfaces of the skin of humans and their fellow primates have the same epidermis-over-dermis pattern. But when you consider the whole body, primate skin can be broken into 2 types: thin skin and thick skin. Thin skin has 4 main layers of epidermal cells and is found on body surfaces that bear hair follicles and oil glands. Thick skin has 5 main layers to its epidermis and is found only on the palms of the hands and soles of the feet, which are scientifically called palmar skin and plantar skin, respectively. Thick skin has many sweat glands but no hair follicles or oil glands.

- On palmar and plantar skin, the interface between the epidermis and dermis has hills and valleys called dermal papillae. The dermal papillae, in turn, project through to the epidermis, creating corresponding surface ridges on palmar and plantar skin called dermatoglyphs. All primates have these friction ridges on the pads of their hands and feet; evolutionarily, they are assumed to help in gripping by increasing surface area for contact.

- Palmar and plantar skin are rich in sweat glands compared to all other body skin, but the sweat is really watery and doesn't directly contribute much to the print. The water in sweat, though, becomes a vehicle to pick up other materials that get deposited in the print. In other words, a fingerprint is really made by the junk that winds up in sweat and clings to the ridges on the skin. Shed skin cells, body oils, and dirt and dust are picked up by sweat when we touch things—including other parts of our body.

- Chemical and thermal burns can destroy prints, but they will leave scars behind. Deep cuts into the dermis, whether intentional or not, will also leave scars. However, the scars that form can be even more distinctive than the original prints were.

The Language of Fingerprints
- To compare and discuss fingerprints, scientists developed a common language to describe and classify the patterns of fingertips. The 3 major fingerprint classifications first used by Galton—arches, loops, and whorls—are still part of modern dactyloscopy, which is the examination and comparison of fingerprints.

- The part of a fingerprint that's categorized runs from the last joint on the palm side of each finger to its tip and then all the way to either side of the nail bed. In other words, there are sides to fingerprints—which is why fingertips are rolled from side to side when someone is fingerprinted.

- There are major and minor features to any fingerprint pattern, and arch, loop, and whorl are considered major features. These describe the overall pattern of the main ridges in a print, especially how they change direction.

© iStockphoto/Thinkstock.

After about 30 minutes of wearing latex gloves, fingerprints can even be laid down through the gloves.

- Some of the 3 main categories are further broken down to give a total of 8 patterns. Smaller features within the major patterns are called minutiae, which add detail to the main pattern of a fingerprint and are behind the comparison science of dactyloscopy.

  o There are plain and tented arches, which are differentiated because a tented arch has almost a vertical core.

  o Loops are subclassified by the direction that they open in. If a loop opens in the direction of the pinkie finger, it's called an ulnar loop because the forearm bone on the little finger side is the ulna. If a loop opens in the direction of the thumb, it's called a radial loop because the forearm bone on the thumb side is the radius.

  o Whorls are more complex and subdivide into 4 types: plain, central pocket, double loop, and accidental.

- Patent prints are prints that can be seen with the unaided eye. They might be made through the friction of skin touching blood, paint, ink, grease, mud, or any semiliquid substance followed by the transfer of that material to a dry surface.

- Latent prints cannot be visualized with the unaided eye and, therefore, have to be developed or enhanced with physical or chemical means.

- Plastic prints are fingerprint impressions that are found on some types of soft materials like chewed gum and wet paint.

- Partial prints could be any type—patent, latent, or plastic—but don't reflect a full fingertip. Most crime-scene prints are partial prints.

- Patent prints can be brought to the lab if they are seen on an object that is easily transported—such as a coffee mug, photo frame, or vehicle—but many crime scenes include prints on surfaces that are difficult or impossible to move—such as a plaster wall or 25-foot-long bank countertop. Most of the time, this type of evidence is collected using only photography.

- Latent prints have to be treated in some way in order to make them visible. One way to find latent prints is by projecting ultraviolet light across a nonabsorbent surface where prints may be hidden. The residues in the fingerprints will reflect the UV light in a different way than the surfaces around them, so prints that can't be seen with the unaided eye might appear.

- Latent prints have to be developed—usually by dusting or through some type of chemical enhancement. Regardless of how prints are developed, they still have to be captured in some way as evidence.

Recording and Comparing Fingerprints
- In order for fingerprints to be useful in forensic investigations, they have to be compared to other prints, so repositories of reference fingerprint records have been collected over time.

- There are many reasons that a person might have a fingerprint record on file—or at least had one made at some point. Fingerprint records are made at the time of arrests, but people who work with large sums of money or other valuables have their prints recorded, too. Prints are also taken for background checks.

- Fingerprints are often taken by simple inking methods on a 10-print card. This standard presentation method collects a rolled print from each finger and both thumbs and a tapped print from the 4 fingers on each hand placed adjacently and then each thumb.

- Since around the early 1990s, digital technologies have been developed. Computerized fingerprint scanners now allow a digit to be put on a digital pad that records the fingerprint. Along with this movement from ink to scanning there have been changes in how prints are stored and compared.

- When comparing prints, either a known or unknown person is compared to the records of known people. However, sometimes unknown prints from a crime scene are matched to other unknown prints from other crime scenes. In these cases, even though the identity of the perpetrator isn't known, the crimes are linked by the prints found at 2 or more scenes.

- Another important use of fingerprint comparisons is to help identify the unknown dead—but only if the body is in good enough shape to allow fingerprinting.

- Fingerprints are also used for security and access purposes, and some high-tech security measures involve scanning a person's prints like a key in a lock to open a door or log on to a computer system.

Fingerprint Coding Systems
- Fingerprint coding systems turn the arch, loop, and whorl patterns on a set of 10 digits into alphabetical and/or numerical codes that can be more quickly and easily compared. This coding allows law enforcement to eliminate huge batches of data without even having to look at the prints the codes represent.

- Codes can also be communicated across distances, and if they don't correlate, then there is no relationship between the prints. If the codes do match, then the actual prints can be compared by hand, side-by-side, to look for minutiae and confirm whether the prints are a true match.

- The Henry system was developed by Sir Edward Henry, head of the Metropolitan Police of London during the early 1900s. The Henry system boils down an entire set of 10 prints into a single fraction that represents the even digits of both hands over the odd digits of both hands. Some version of the original Henry system is still used in most European countries and by the U.S. Federal Bureau of Investigation.

- As computer technologies like scanning have improved, computerized matching of prints have become possible. In 1999, the U.S. FBI developed its Integrated Automated Fingerprint Identification System (IAFIS).

- As powerful as IAFIS is, it has its limitations. Fingerprint quality—particularly from scene prints—is often lacking, and IAFIS really only searches on ridge patterns, not all minutiae. A law enforcement officer or forensic scientist still has to view any IAFIS system-suggested matches and critically examine them.

- It's not only fingers that leave prints; people's palms also have unique prints. This is also true with the soles of the feet. Even lip prints—from a coffee mug or lipstick mark, for example—have been used to link a person to a scene or object.

Questions to Consider

1. Do all primates have fingerprints?

2. Do identical twins have the same fingerprints?

3. At what point in human development do fingerprints occur?

4. What are the 3 main classes into which fingerprints are categorized?

5. Are your fingerprints on file anywhere?

Telltale Marks—Tools, Guns, and Ammunition
Lecture 4

In forensic science, a toolmark is some type of evidence—a cut, gouge, abrasion, or impression—that is left by a tool on something it contacts. Much of the science of firearms identification is actually a subcategory of toolmark analysis because a gun is really a tool that leaves its marks on the bullet and the bullet's cartridge case every time it fires a round. Forensic toolmark examination relies mainly on the overall shape of a tool and the combination of manufacturing and use defects on it.

Toolmark Basics

- Toolmarks usually take the form of impression and striated marks on a softer surface that the tool was used on. Locard's principle states that tools can also cause a physical exchange of materials between the 2 surfaces that come in contact. Toolmarks and any transferred trace evidence involved can be obvious or microscopic—depending on the tool, substrate, and actions involved during the exchange between the tool and its target.

- When a toolmark is large enough to be seen with the unaided eye, it usually offers some class characteristics, such as the general shape or size of the tool, but a microscopic examination of a toolmark gives much more detail and might even allow a suspected match to be developed between a specific tool and the object it was used on.

- No 2 tools are completely identical—not even those made by the same manufacturer in the same batch. Likewise, no 2 toolmarks are completely identical—not even those from the same tool used repeatedly during a single crime. The repeated use of a single tool involves different angles, and different amounts of force are applied each time.

- The tool changes the surface of what it's used against and leaves marks behind, but the tool itself can also be altered during the course of the crime in both obvious and microscopic ways.

Tools and Crime Scenes
- The tools that are found by investigators at crime scenes are usually easy to transport to the crime lab, but the surfaces the toolmarks are on may or may not be easily transported. Toolmark scene documentation, as with all crime scenes, involves careful photography with a measuring scale in place.

- If the situation warrants—as in the case of evidence that isn't easily transported—investigators can attempt to make a highly detailed cast of the toolmark using a casting material, such as liquid silicone or dental plaster, at the scene. Having only a cast to work from, however, can dilute the evidence and reduce the ability to make a definitive association with a suspect tool, if it is found.

- The packaging and transportation of evidence is critical, too. The tool and whatever it was used on have to be packaged separately to prevent any further interaction—and because a tool can hold important trace evidence such as microscopic chips of paint, fiber evidence, or even blood and other body tissues.

- The crime scene investigator should never try to fit the suspected tool back into the toolmark—not at the scene or in the lab—because doing so could alter the mark and compromise the investigation. Instead, at the lab, toolmark experts can use a suspected tool to make test markings for comparison, which allows the direct comparison between known and unknown toolmarks.

- It's not easy for toolmark examiners in a laboratory to exactly duplicate a toolmark left at a crime scene, but the use of a soft material, such as lead, allows an impression to be made of the edge of a recovered tool without damaging it or creating additional use or wear.

- Investigators can also use a piece of the original substrate to try to create a duplicate of the toolmark. In other words, they might try to replicate the toolmark by not only using the suspected tool, but also by using a piece of the same surface from the crime scene.

- Just as in fingerprint analysis, when investigators find a sufficient number of similarities between the test markings and the evidentiary marks from the crime scene, an association can be made. Careful documentation of the lab-created toolmarks and the ones taken from the crime scene are necessary—in case they are needed in court.

Firearms Examination

- When a projectile travels through the barrel of a gun, microscopic marks called striae are created on the bullet and on its cartridge casing; therefore, each bullet is changed and etched as it is fired—much like the way the machining of a tool creates unique microscopic properties during manufacturing.

- Firearms examination and the science of ballistics are not the same. Ballistics is a subdivision of physics that explains the way an object travels—whether it's a baseball or a bullet.

- In general, there are 5 main groups of firearms and countless different types of ammunition.

  o Pistols, which are sometimes called handguns, are subclassified as either revolvers or self-loading pistols.

  o Rifles are similar to pistols but have a longer barrel and are meant to be used with 2 hands.

  o Machine guns are automatic weapons that are fed ammunition from either a magazine (clip) or a belt.

  o Submachine guns are also fully automatic but can be handheld.

o Shotguns are very different because they don't fire bullets; instead, they fire pellets, buckshot, or slugs.

- Firearms investigators may need to document the general condition of a recovered weapon, including checking to see if it is even capable of being fired, if it has been made illegal by modifications, or if something was wrong with a firearm that might have caused it to discharge accidentally.

© iStockphoto/Thinkstock.

- Firearms examiners may also try to restore the serial number of a weapon—or any object that might have a serial number stamped into its metal—because criminals often try

The cartridge casings of self-loading pistols are ejected from the chamber automatically as each bullet is fired from the barrel.

to file the serial number off of a stolen gun. However, even if the serial number seems obliterated, the process that created the serial number leaves traces in the form of permanent stress marks in the metal that can be restored.

- A large focus of firearms examination is whether a particular weapon fired a certain round of ammunition that was recovered. This is when investigators try to match bullets recovered from a crime scene or victim—or casings that were fired—to figure out whether they came from a weapon in question.

The Makings and Workings of Firearms
- Surface irregularities produced during the manufacturing process can make it possible for a forensic investigator to tie a bullet to a particular gun—to the exclusion of all others.

- The barrel of a gun is initially produced by hollowing out a solid metal bar, which is done by a drill that leaves individual random marks on the inside of the barrel. In addition, the inner surface of a gun barrel is imprinted with a series of spiral grooves through a manufacturing process called rifling.

- Inside the barrel of a gun, the raised regions resulting from the rifling process are known as lands, and the valleys are known as grooves.

- When used as a verb, the term "rifling" means the spin that's put on a flying object—whether on a football or a bullet—by encouraging the twist with a series of raised objects. In the case of a gun, the rifling ridges inside the barrel produce the spin on a bullet, which helps the bullet stay on a true trajectory and maintain its velocity.

- The internal diameter of a firearm barrel is known as the gun's caliber—as measured between the lands. Caliber is usually expressed in either hundredths of an inch or in millimeters.

- Shotguns are not measured in the same way. Their barrel diameter is called gauge, which is the measure of the number of lead pellets of the diameter of the barrel that together would weigh 1 pound.

- When a bullet is fired, the barrel's lands and grooves make corresponding marks on the surface of the bullet as it is spiraled down the length of the barrel. The raised lands in the gun barrel etch matching grooves on the bullet, and the depressed grooves in the barrel create raised lands on the bullet.

- Firearms manufacturers choose specific rifling processes to meet their weapons' specifications, so by knowing the specifics of different gun manufacturers, a firearms examiner might be easily able to tell the class characteristics on a bullet as having been fired from a certain brand of gun—but class characteristics aren't unique to a specific weapon.

- Despite large-scale manufacturing operations, random minute markings produced mostly by drilling make the inside of one gun barrel different from another. These microscopic manufacturing imperfections result in individual characteristics that can tie a specific bullet to a specific gun.

- In order to match a bullet or cartridge case from a crime scene to a given gun, a firearms expert has to test fire the gun, using the same type of ammo, and then compare the bullet fired at the crime lab to the bullet from the scene. The expert has to fire the gun into something that will trap the bullet without damaging it.

Guns, Ammunition, Propellants, and Primers
- Bullets and shotgun pellets can be found at crime scenes—perhaps lodged in a victim, a wall, or a piece of furniture. Just as with toolmarks, if the bullet is lodged in something or someone that can be transported to the forensic lab or morgue, that's always the approach taken.

- Bullets, cartridge cases, cartridges, and guns must all be handled and documented very carefully to preserve any trace evidence that might be present. This could include fingerprints of the victim or shooter as well as blood or tissue that might be on the gun or in its barrel.

- The propellants and primers that are used in firearms are important in forensics because they constitute gunshot residue (GSR), which exits the barrel as a mixture of the partially burned and unburned powder, soot, lead, and lead vapors from the ammunition.

- Because the residue disperses in a geometric pattern as it leaves the barrel, it can help identify the distance between a weapon and its target. The primer can also leave lead, barium, and antimony residue on things or people that are within close proximity and can aid in forensic investigations.

- In the early 1990s, the Bureau of Alcohol, Tobacco, Firearms, and Explosives in the United States developed the Integrated Ballistics Identification System, which allows microscopic images of bullet land and groove rifling impressions to be compared across the Internet.

- By the late 1990s, this system was linked with one developed by the U.S. Federal Bureau of Investigation to examine firing pin and primer impressions on spent cartridge casings. These 2 tools have revolutionized the work of firearms examiners and have allowed the national networking of investigations—in much the same way that IAFIS revolutionized the fingerprinting process.

Suggested Reading

Heard, *Handbook of Firearms and Ballistics*.

Questions to Consider

1. Are tool marks an example of class or individuating evidence?

2. How is toolmark evidence preserved, especially if it's on something that is not easily transported?

3. About how many gun-related crimes occur in the United States each year?

4. What are some specific reasons that a firearms expert might need to examine a gun?

Good Impressions—Shoes, Tires, and Skin
Lecture 5

In addition to fingerprints, toolmarks, and bullets, shoe prints, tire marks, and fabric impressions also constitute impression evidence and can be used in forensic investigations. Impression evidence found at crime scenes can be any kind of pattern made by—or found in—soil, dust, snow, blood, wet paint, and many other media. Just as with other kinds of evidence, impressions made by shoe prints and tire treads show general features that give class information, including the manufacturer, size, and brand. Furthermore, as with tools and firearms, shoes and tires also gain individuating characteristics as they're used and worn over time.

Impression Evidence
- Like many other types of analyses, looking at impression evidence—such as shoe prints, tire marks, and fabric impressions—typically involves comparing an unknown pattern from a crime scene with a known exemplar shoe print or tire track that is intentionally taken off a suspect's person, footwear, or vehicle.

- This kind of impression work can also involve getting exclusionary shoe prints or tire tracks from people or cars that are not related to the criminal act but were at the scene for a legitimate reason.

- Not only might shoe prints or tire tracks be easier to locate than fingerprints or microscopic striae that may be left on tools or bullets at a crime scene, but there are probably many more footprints left behind at a crime scene than fingerprints, toolmarks, or bullets because feet often make more contact with surfaces in an environment than hands do.

- However, shoes can be thrown away after a crime is committed whereas fingerprints don't change, and it's generally easier to wipe off your fingerprints than to get rid of shoe prints—but a backtracking burglar could do either.

General Forensic Photography Techniques

- One of the greatest problems that investigators might run into with impression evidence is preserving and documenting the scene. Typically, shoe prints and tire tracks have to be carefully photographed by a competent crime-scene photographer because if the material the print or track is on can't be moved—or if the substrate is temporary, such as snow—then the photographs might be the only source for future comparisons or at trial.

- Over the past decade, crime-scene photography has moved from black-and-white Polaroid instant cameras to state-of-the-art digital technology.

- There are a handful of basic principles of forensic photography that are common to most scenes.

  - A forensic photographer has to keep a careful log that tracks the pictures taken at a crime scene—including when, where, and by whom.

  - Usually, images start with broad overviews to give perspective and show relationships between things at the scene. Then, they progress to medium shots that are taken from about 6 feet away. Close-up shots—from about 1 foot or less away—are taken where detailed views are needed.

  - Photographs have to include a measuring scale so that the exact size of things can be shown. It's fairly common to take a duplicate picture without the scale just to show things as they were before the scale was there. Only with an accurate scale can things in photos be compared later, with any confidence, to other images or objects.

  - Photographs should be taken from a few different angles and use both direct and side lighting to maximize detail, which is particularly important with impression evidence. In addition, side lighting can show more of the 3-dimensionality of evidence.

o   Images should be taken in a 360° pattern from a fixed point using a wide-angle lens and tripod so that pictures can be overlapped to show the entire scene in every direction.

o   Special attention needs to be given to entrance and exit routes in the beginning because it might be difficult to preserve those areas and still get full access to the site. In addition, at an indoor crime scene, any adjacent rooms or spaces should be photographed because they could be routes the perpetrator used to get to the scene.

o   Any physical evidence—including a body—needs to have full photo documentation before it's moved, and whoever discovered the crime scene or the body has to be questioned to see if he or she moved anything in his or her effort to figure out what was going on.

o   The general rule of thumb—especially now that photography has gone digital—is that you can never have too many pictures of a scene or the evidence in it, so take as many as possible.

o   Digital photography and videophotography have become standard ways of documenting crime scenes, but videotaping shouldn't replace still photography. Forensics needs the resolution that only still images can provide.

Lifting and Casting Evidence
- Sometimes, there's no way evidence can be transported to the lab from the crime scene, but there are some cases where shoe print or tire-track evidence is portable.

- When shoe prints or tire tracks can't be moved, after the photographer is finished, investigators might try lifting or casting 3-D evidence, and they often get only one chance to correctly do so.

- If an impression is made in a thin layer of dust or dirt, investigators can try an adhesive lifting material and put it over all or part of the impression—just as a fingerprint can be lifted—but electrostatic lifting technology can also be used.

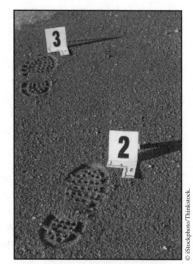

It is extremely difficult to access a crime scene on foot without disturbing latent footprints.

- When a footprint or tire track is not on a flat, dusty surface, lifting it with an adhesive or by an electrostatic process doesn't work. When there's a lot of 3-dimensionality to an impression and it can't be moved back to the lab, casting is the best way to preserve the evidence.

- Dental stone—the gypsum material dentists use to make molds of people's teeth—is the preferred casting material. Dental stone gives better detail and makes more durable casts than most other options.

- For very fragile or transient prints, there are some commercially available waxy sprays that seal footprints or tire tracks when they occur in a substrate like snow, and then the sealed impression can be casted.

- Casting methods mostly involve pouring the casting material over the 3-D surface of the impression and letting it harden. After the cast is dry, investigators do a detailed examination of it. If it is a

35

good impression, it should be as close to a copy of the original surface as possible.

- When you step in something like soft mud, you make a negative impression of the sole of your shoe in the mud—much like a mirror reversal. However, if you cast your footprint, the cast makes a negative of the original negative, forming a positive image that matches—not mirrors—your shoe.

- If impression evidence is located on a steep incline, the casting material is going to follow gravity, so some engineering might be necessary—such as building a wooden frame around the footprint and then filling the box with casting material. In addition, removing any debris from the impression without disturbing the evidence can be an obstacle that complicates the casting process.

Comparing Impression Evidence
- There are 3 comparison possibilities to consider.

  o First, evidence is recovered from a crime scene, but a plausible suspect who might have similar evidence to match it is never found.

  o Secondly, an investigation might lead to a good suspect in a case, but that person either didn't leave much recoverable evidence or the right kind of evidence at the scene.

  o The third comparison possibility is the backbone of forensic investigation: Evidence is found at a crime scene, and later, a suspected person, tool, weapon, or shoe is discovered to have the identical properties of the crime-scene evidence.

- Like other kinds of forensic comparisons, investigators like to use test impressions to make quality comparisons between an impression from an unknown shoe or tire associated with a crime and a comparable object they want to compare to it.

- One of the ways that shoe prints and tire marks are similar to guns and ammunition—but are different from fingerprints—is that shoes and tires come in standard sizes and are made by manufacturers that work toward quality control and brand identity in how they make their products.

- The style and size of a shoe or a tire can give class characteristics. Once investigators know the brand, the measurements of and between the small jagged lines on the bottom of a shoe can let investigators figure out its size. Then, investigators might be able to contact the manufacturer to tell exactly when and where that type of shoe was produced.

- However, even if the suspect has the exact same kind of shoe in his or her closet, the style and size alone aren't individuating evidence. In other words, that similarity doesn't usually put the suspect at the scene.

- Just as with tools and guns, a shoe develops unique use characteristics when it is worn over time, so investigators might get lucky—especially if the shoe is not new or is discovered right after the crime was committed. Small gouges, cuts, and other kinds of wear marks found on a well-worn shoe might be able to be matched specifically to crime-scene evidence.

- This kind of pattern evidence comparison rises to a much higher level of certainty. Just as with fingerprints or the microscopic rifling marks on a bullet, when enough points of comparison can be made between the unknown footwear evidence and a test pattern made from a known shoe, there might be enough for reasonable people to say that this shoe—and only this shoe—was used at the crime scene.

- The ability of investigators to identify the make and model of a tire from its tread could ultimately lead them to a particular kind of vehicle, and because cars are registered to owners, a tire track might actually lead to a suspect in a way that a shoe print probably couldn't. More than likely, though, even if a tire can be matched to its manufacturer and style, many vehicles would have that brand of tire.

- In comparison to the first tires that were made by Dunlop in 1888 and didn't have any tread, today's tires are much more complex in construction and can vary a lot in size. For example, the coding on the sidewall of a tire describes the type of vehicle that the tire is made for along with some of its dimensions and other design features.

- Databases of tire details have been developed to help identify vehicles in forensic work. Because of the repetition on a tire's surface, it might not take much of a pattern to figure out the kind or brand of tire—and from that, perhaps the kind of vehicle—that made the track.

- With impression evidence, it's occasionally possible that a fabric imprint gets transferred to the surface of a vehicle that strikes a pedestrian, especially if the fabric has a unique 3-D surface. Textile marks can be left on skin and might be seen during an autopsy or in the emergency room. Things like belts, ropes, jewelry, zippers, and buttons can leave impression evidence on skin.

- Sometimes, impression evidence on human skin can't be seen with the unaided eye without alternate light source photography, which involves taking pictures under ultraviolet or infrared light.

Suggested Reading

Bodziak, *Footwear Impression Evidence.*

———, *Tire Tread and Tire Track Evidence.*

1. In addition to fingerprints and tool marks, what other kinds of impression evidence might be found at a crime scene?

2. Can you think of examples in which impression evidence would be temporary or transient? If so, how would the evidence be preserved?

3. How is forensic photography different from other types of photography?

Forensics of Fibers, Paint, and Glass
Lecture 6

Unlike impression evidence, trace evidence—such as fibers, paint, and glass—is physical bits of material that can be left behind in minute quantities. Even tiny bits of polymer or glass evidence can usually be matched to comparable substances by common class characteristics to indicate chemical makeup, manufacturer, and location of sale. Occasionally, when larger pieces of fabric, paint, or glass are found, they can be individualized to the definitive source they came from at the exclusion of all others.

Forms of Trace Evidence

- Fibers—from natural and man-made sources—and paint are chemically similar. They're both polymers, which means that they are made of long chains of repeating subunit molecules called monomers that are linked together by chemical bonds.

- Many natural and synthetic materials are polymers, including many of the carbohydrates and all of the proteins we eat. Polymers also make up many structures in and on our bodies—such as muscle proteins, hair, DNA, plastics, rubbers, paints, varnishes, shellacs, stains, and some inks.

- Glass is not a polymer; it's a composite substance called an amorphous solid that is made mostly of sand—often with the addition of soda and lime.

- Glass and polymers, like paint and textile fibers, are common types of trace evidence that can be found on clothes, shoes, floors, and other surfaces. These bits of evidence can be directly deposited from a primary source or moved around by different modes of transfer.

Classifying and Analyzing Fiber Evidence

- After the usual documentation, including careful photography, fiber evidence can be removed from its surface at the crime scene if investigators see it—but often it's better to take surfaces that might hold fibers back to the lab.

- A brush can be used to extract anything that comes off of clothing, and cellophane tape can be used to pull off only surface material. Vacuuming picks up more than tape, but it results in many more fibers to look through under a microscope. If a stray fiber is obvious—on clothes or anywhere else—forceps can be used to directly pick it up for examination.

- Fibers can be broken down into 5 major types.

  o There are many types of plant fibers used in textiles, such as cotton, flax, hemp, jute, ramie, and papyrus.

  o Some fibers have an animal origin, such as wool and silk.

  o Synthetic fibers are completely man-made and include polyester, nylon, rayon, and many others.

  o There are also blends, such as a blend of polyester and cotton.

  o Fibers that aren't used in clothing but could still be found as evidence are man-made mineral fibers in fiberglass, which is sometimes called glass wool.

- Fibers can also be distinguished by their color and weave, which relate to the kind of processes used on the base materials during manufacturing. Individual fiber types are actually fairly rare in their frequency in the environment with one notable exception: indigo-dyed cotton denim.

- Microscopic analysis is used by forensic scientists as a nondestructive way to get a lot of information about the fibers that make up a fabric. Under a microscope, fibers—like many other compounds—react differently to different types of light.

- A microscope can establish the precise width of the fiber because measuring tools, known as micrometers, can be put inside microscopes. Microscopy also shows differences in the cross-sectional anatomy of fibers.

Fibers from clothing and other types of man-made materials are commonly found as trace evidence at crime scenes.

- Microscope examination might also document damage, making it possible to determine if a fabric has been intentionally cut or pulled apart. Microscopy might also identify any foreign material, such as soil or blood, that might not be visible to the unaided eye.

- There are many chemical tests that aid in fiber identification, but they are only done after nondestructive techniques are used. Chemical tests essentially break the fiber down to figure out what's in it. For example, chromatography involves separating the subcomponents in a mixture.

- By combining all of the various methods of testing—microscopy, optical properties, and chemistry—forensic scientists can often hone in on and identify specific fiber types. However, analysts cannot state with 100% certainty that a fiber came from a specific source because of the mass production of garments and textiles.

- When an actual fragment of clothing is recovered as evidence, investigators can get lucky with a tear match, where the evidence fits together like a puzzle—if they can find the garment the cloth fragment came from.

Classifying and Analyzing Paint Evidence

- Although paint is a polymer that begins with long chains, just like fibers do, paint has other cross-linkages that hold the strands together into a sheet.

- In forensic terms, there are 3 main categories of paint: automotive paint, structural paint—what's found on buildings, walls, furniture, and mailboxes—and artistic paint, which can be important in cases involving art forgeries.

- Chemically, paint is a collection of pigments and additives that is suspended in a binder with a consistency that's adjusted by a solvent, which allows it to change from a liquid to a solid.

- Forensic scientists deal with automotive paint most often. Manufacturers and refurbishers use specific chemicals, different sequences of layers of paint, and different thicknesses of layers. The complicated nature of automotive paint usually makes it much easier to match than other types of paint.

- There are some things about collecting paint evidence that mirror fiber evidence collection—such as taking the whole surface with the paint on it to the lab, if possible. However, if the paint is embedded in the road or on a phone pole, a scalpel can be used to carefully slice off a sliver of asphalt or phone pole because without the full layering, an analyst doesn't get the whole picture.

- One way that paint evidence collection differs from textiles is that crime-scene investigators should not use a tape lift because the chemicals and adhesives in the tape can make some paint tests difficult.

- For a car accident, samples from all involved cars should be taken from an undamaged area of the car as close as possible to the damaged area, especially if there's a chance any part of the car has been repainted. At the lab, forensic scientists can use a thin blade to cut a paint sample at an angle to better see the layers.

- As with fibers, the order of paint testing is sometimes determined by how large of a sample the lab has to work with. Microscopy is used first so that the layers can be examined and compared. Investigators compare known and unknown samples to see if they match in condition, color, wear, texture, and layering. After microscopic analysis, there are many chemical and high-tech instrumental methods that can be used.

- If there's no known sample for comparison, law enforcement agencies can use a database called the paint data query (PDQ) to potentially identify the year, make, and model of a car.

Classifying and Analyzing Glass Evidence

- There are estimated to be over 700 different types of glass, and only about 70 of those are used commonly. For investigators, it's the rare types that are most distinctive as forensic evidence.

- As an amorphous solid, glass doesn't contain crystals and doesn't have any other type of ordered structure. Glass is made from fused inorganic materials—mostly silicon oxides, which are better known as sand, and some metal oxides. These are melted together at high temperatures and then cooled without crystallization.

- Depending on the size of a piece of broken glass, some features can be discerned with the unaided eye, and other details can only be seen through microscopic analysis. To narrow glass to a source, investigators look at many different properties, including thickness, color, texture, design, curvature, and tinting.

- Microscopy can also show debris, such as gunpowder residue or soil, on glass fragments, and unless it's recently been cleaned, the amount of debris can usually help identify which side of a piece of window glass was the outside surface.

- The way glass fractures can also tell something about its makeup. Tempered safety glass is made stronger than ordinary window glass by rapid heating and cooling of surfaces so that it breaks into small squares or spheres instead of shards with sharp edges. Laminated glass is used in car windshields; it has a layer of plastic between 2 pieces of window glass, so it also breaks differently.

- Like paint, the additives in glass—including sodium, calcium, boron, and tin—give it different properties and can be useful in forensic glass identification.

- The refractive index and density of glass are the 2 most important properties that forensic examiners look at. The refractive index is the result of the way the speed of light changes when it goes through a material. Light refracts, or bends, as it passes through glass. The refractive index is also why objects look different above and below the surface of water.

- The density of glass, or any other material, can be determined with a float test, which involves floating an unknown glass fragment in a series of clear, gradient columns filled with liquids of known density. The glass fragment stops dropping in the density gradient when it reaches its own density.

- The FBI laboratory created a database of refractive index and density values that can help narrow down the type and frequency of use of the glass involved in a crime.

- If an investigator has large enough pieces of broken glass, he or she might be able to put the pieces back together like a jigsaw puzzle to re-create all or part of whatever was broken.

- Sometimes, examiners can figure out whether glass breakage was due to a high- or low-velocity impact. In high-velocity impacts, there's usually a cone, or crater, effect, in which the smaller opening—the top of the cone—is on the side of the glass that was first hit by the impact, and the larger opening—the base of the cone—is on the exit side of the glass.

- The same principles can be used when analyzing bone trauma—especially when examining the skull for high-velocity trauma like gunshot wounds. When a bullet passes through a skull, it's as if it is passing through 2 pieces of glass—with one representing the entrance wound and the other representing the exit wound.

- With gunshots through both glass and bone, the diameter of the hole can't be directly correlated with the caliber of a bullet, other than to give a maximum possible size, because you can't end up with a hole that's smaller than the bullet itself.

- Examiners can sometimes establish the order of multiple impacts, in both glass and skull fractures, using radial and concentric fractures. Radial fractures extend out like rays from the initial point of impact while concentric fractures are circular fractures around the point of impact.

Suggested Reading

Caddy, ed., *Forensic Examination of Glass and Paint*.

Questions to Consider

1. What is the physical makeup of glass?

2. Can broken glass be class evidence or individuating evidence?

3. What types of polymers constitute crime-scene evidence?

Traces of Hair and Fur
Lecture 7

Among the many varieties of trace evidence, hair is one of the most commonly analyzed forms of trace evidence. One of the great values of hair in forensic science is that it's very stable when compared to other body tissues. However, if 2 hairs are similar, it does not automatically indicate that someone is guilty, but it will allow investigators to continue to focus on the person as a suspect and gather additional evidence, including DNA testing, to either prove the guilt or support the innocence of the suspect.

The Structure of Hair

- Hair is a unique feature of mammals that is abundant in some animals and less abundant in other species, including whales and modern humans. There's really no difference between hair and fur—except that fur typically refers to the hair of nonhuman mammals.

- Hair form differs not only among different types of mammals, but also within different regions of the same animal's body. Humans have many different types of hair on their bodies—including eyebrows, eyelashes, beard hair, and body hair—but only pubic and scalp hair are typically analyzed in a forensic lab. The other types don't have enough internal detail for meaningful comparisons.

- Hair has interesting growth patterns and functions. Some hairs on the body have a long lifespan with near continuous growth—such as beard hair and head hair—but other hairs—such as arm and leg hairs, eyebrows, and eyelashes—have a fairly consistent and relatively short length on an individual and are shed and replaced once they achieve that length.

- All hairs have a nerve ending at their root, so hairs act as a means of sensation; in other words, hair allows us to feel the approach of something before it actually comes in direct contact with our skin. This is one reason hair may be found at a crime scene.

- Human hair, like that of other mammals, is a dead extension of the skin made mostly of proteins. The main protein is keratin, which is a widespread component of the body coverings of many animals—including reptile scales, bird feathers and beaks, cat claws, primate fingernails, and rhino horns. Other proteins in hair, such as melanin, give it color.

- The root of the hair is anchored into the dermis layer of the skin, which is surrounded by epidermal cells that make up the follicle. Blood vessels at the hair root transport the raw materials for hair production and growth.

- Because the substances needed to build hair come from the bloodstream, hair becomes a lasting repository of certain chemicals in the body. This can include illicit drugs, such as THC from marijuana, and certain poisons, such as arsenic, that can be incorporated into the shaft of the hair as it grows.

- If there is a suspicion of drug use or poisoning, chemical analyses can be performed on hair during drug testing or at autopsy. Blood and urine samples can show only a relatively recent history of drug use or toxins in the body, but the chemical stability of hair makes it an excellent and long-standing record of body chemistry.

- Because hair growth rates are fairly standard, investigators are able to roughly date when a chemical substance was laid down in hair. References vary on the typical rate of scalp hair growth, but estimates range from about 1 to 1.25 centimeters a month, which is about 0.5 inches.

The Life Stages of Hair
- At any given time, most hairs are in an actively growing stage called the anagen phase, in which new cells are being added at the hair root, pushing the hair shaft further toward the body surface.

The anagen growth phase can last as long as 2 to 7 years for scalp hair, depending on the type of body hair and possibly genetics.

- If a hair is pulled forcibly during this growth phase, a follicle tag will remain on the ribbon-like end of the hair root; you may have seen this white residue if you have plucked an eyebrow. In violent crimes in which people struggle with each other, hair may be pulled out and left at the crime scene or transferred from one person to another.

- Near the end of a hair's life cycle, it enters the catagen phase, where growth begins to slow down. During the catagen phase, the hair root begins to shrivel away from the follicle and becomes elongated.

- The final phase in the life of a single hair is the telogen phase and is the time when a hair is getting ready to be shed naturally. It breaks away from the follicle, and the root takes on a more bulbous shape. A hair may remain lodged in its follicle in the telogen stage for several months before actually falling out.

- Numbers of typical hairs lost per day range from a few dozen to 100 or more, depending on age and health, and it takes about 6 months to regrow a full scalp of hair.

- Telogen hairs are typically the type found at crime scenes and analyzed in case samples. In fact, depending on the amount of body hair a person has and how often that person vacuums, there may be hundreds or even thousands of shed hairs in someone's home or vehicle at any given time.

- However, shed hairs can easily be transferred from one place to another by an object or person that the hair doesn't belong to. In that sense, hair is always circumstantial evidence.

The Microscopic Anatomy of Hair

- The 3 main regions of a hair are the cuticle, cortex, and medulla. The cuticle of a hair is made up of scales that have the microscopic appearance of a shingled roof.

- All humans have the same cuticle pattern, so looking at the cuticle of a human hair is no help in identification. However, nonhuman animals have different cuticle patterns that can be observed microscopically to differentiate among nonhuman hairs.

- Beneath the cuticle, the cortex of a hair is made up of many cells that are regularly arranged parallel to the hair's length, giving the hair most of its strength. Looking at the cortex is a critical part of hair comparison because the cortex contains the pigment granules that give hair much of its color.

Hair may be found or analyzed years after a death or crime because it is such a stable form of trace evidence.

- When hair is bleached, it loses pigmentation from its cortex. When hair is dyed, the color can either coat the surface or penetrate into the cortex, depending on the type of hair color used. Only the portion of the hair that is treated will show color change. At examination, therefore, the root end will not only show the true color, but also the line where it was dyed. Untreated regrowth also shows the original color of the hair.

- The core of a hair, known as the medulla, is a hollow region at its center. In humans, the medulla takes up only about 1/3 of the total diameter of the hair, but in most nonhuman mammals, the medullary index—the fraction of the medulla when compared to the hair shaft—is more than 1/2. In general, human scalp hairs either have no medulla or a fragmented medulla.

- Telling the difference between hairs from different parts of the human body is fairly easy—sometimes with the unaided eye—by using characteristics such as length, texture, color, and diameter, but there are underlying microscopic differences that relate to the obvious differences that can be seen.

- The ends of hair that have been cut or shaved have a blunt tip while body hairs that are not have a naturally tapered end, and scalp hairs that are long and not recently cut usually show a frayed end—often called a split end.

- Knowing the average rate of hair growth, investigators can gauge the age of a hair by its length. However, the age or sex of the person that the hair belongs to can't be judged with any confidence—except maybe for the very fine hairs found on the scalp of a baby. Even gray hair doesn't necessarily relate solely to a person's age.

Hair Comparison
- There are specific steps involved in a hair comparison. First, a questioned hair has to be identified among all the evidence at a scene, which can actually be difficult, and then the unknown hair has to be classified by type—such as head or pubic hair—and be assessed to determine which tests it's likely suitable for.

- Then, a representative group of known standards of the same type of hair—head or pubic—have to be taken from a suspect or someone who investigators need to exclude.

- If there are similar features, they should be noted before a microscopic exam. If there are not similar features, the comparison is concluded and the report is issued. However, if the questioned and known hairs warrant a complete comparison, then they have to be examined microscopically.

- Using a side-by-side comparison microscope, detailed observations can be made using all of the features of the cortex and its pigment distribution as well as the medulla and its form.

- An investigator has 3 options with regard to reporting on the comparison between any 2 hairs.

  o If there are no unexplainable differences and many commonalities between 2 hairs in question, a trace analyst may conclude that the 2 hairs could have come from the same person.

  o If there are clear differences that go beyond the typical range of variation seen in a single person, then an analyst may conclude that the 2 hairs could not have come from the same individual.

  o If there are both similarities and differences, then no conclusion can be made about a potential association between the hair in question and hairs taken from a known person.

- Investigators have attempted to classify hair in much the same way that fingerprints are categorized, but human hair can't be fit into any reasonable number of classes to allow for discrete categories the way they've been able to do with fingerprints and genetic markers.

- Furthermore, when people change their hair—or as it changes naturally when they age—the hair changes class groups. This is different from fingerprints and genetic markers, which don't change as people age.

- To come up with a good hair standard for a single person, many known hairs are needed because even on the same person's scalp, any number of hairs might vary in diameter, length, and color.

- An investigator should collect at least 50 full-length, intact hairs—which means with the root—from the scalp of a single subject to serve as that person's known reference sample. Because of regional differences, these hairs should come from a variety of locations on the person's head.

- Similarities between hairs can be noted and dissimilarities between hairs can definitely provide exclusions, but there is currently nothing short of nuclear DNA technology to positively link a hair to a specific person.

Suggested Reading

Robertson, *Forensic Examination of Hair*.

Questions to Consider

1. What do hair and fur have in common, and how are they different?

2. If someone's hair is found at a crime scene, is it conclusive evidence that the person was at that location?

3. What types of information can be gained from the examination of hair?

4. Is hair an example of class or individuating evidence?

Soil, Protist, Plant, and Animal Traces
Lecture 8

E lements such as hair and fur from various animals are useful in forensic investigations, but there are many more ways in which the natural world is involved in forensic science. Soil, wood, pollen grains, animal hairs, and single-celled organisms called protists can all be used to link a person or object to a crime scene. Animals are used directly in some investigations—particularly insects, which forensic entomologists use to estimate time of death—and, of course, larger animals are investigated as suspects if they are accused of attacking people.

Analyzing Soil

- Soil is a mixture composed of both natural inorganic and organic materials but can also include man-made materials. The inorganic stuff in soil is mostly decaying or weathered rocks and minerals. Because they tend to vary geographically, the types and percentages of rocks and minerals can indicate a possible location associated with a suspect or victim.

- Soil testing requires experience and skill in a variety of microscopic, physical, and chemical-testing methods. Forensic investigators— and sometimes geologists, soil scientists, or archaeologists—test the questioned soil to determine where it was originally found and, therefore, where known samples should be taken from for comparison.

- Depending on the type of test being done, the soil may need to be pulverized and homogenized, but this can only be done after any tests that require the soil to be untouched are finished.

- Soils can vary a lot in color; it's estimated that there are over 1000 distinguishable soil colors. The Munsell system, which was developed by Alfred Munsell and adopted by the U.S. Department of Agriculture, uses 3 main descriptors with regard to color: hue, value, and purity.

- Soils also vary in texture: Some are loamy like garden soil while others are silty like soil from a creek or river. In addition, particle size differs in soils, and this can be measured using a graduated set of mesh soil sieves.

- Furthermore, the specific rocks and minerals in soil can be examined. Fracture patterns are the ways pieces of rock and minerals break off, leaving jagged or smooth edges. The optical properties, such as refractive index, can also be examined; some grains appear to be different colors at different angles.

Soil that is found on the tires of a vehicle can be analyzed to possibly link a car to the scene of a crime.

Analyzing Pollen, Spores, and Protists

- Palynology is the study of pollen and spores, but it can also include the study of other microscopic organisms in soil and water. Pollen grains are the male gametes of seed-bearing plants, which include all flowering plants and cone-bearing plants. Spores are the reproductive units of lower plants like fungi, ferns, and mosses. Some protists also reproduce using spores.

- Pollen and spores make good forensic evidence because they both have durable coverings that resist being degraded in the environment, and localities have distinctive plant and fungus

55

distributions, so they have distinctive pollen and spores. Different populations of protists in a sample of soil or water may even point to a specific season because plants and fungi reproduce at specific times of the year.

- Soil or water samples that include pollen grains, fungal spores, and protists need to be examined microscopically using a typical light microscope for general structure and a scanning electron microscope (SEM) for 3-D detail. Distinctive features usually include the size and complexity of these biological bits of evidence.

- If a body is found in the bushes, but the pollen on the clothing doesn't match the type of bushes it's found in, the body might have been moved from somewhere else to its current location.

- Furthermore, if the clothing can be assessed for the specific types and amounts of pollen and spores, analysts may be able to come up with a general profile of the type of area and the plants in it that investigators should be looking for.

- Characterizing the microscopic life forms, including pollen, spores, and protists, in the clothing or the airway of a body that was in water might lead investigators to a possible location—or at least tell them more about how or where the person died or where the body has been.

Analyzing Wood
- Some forensic specialists can identify species of trees and other woody plants by the microscopic patterns seen in

In addition to pollen, wood is another type of plant evidence that has forensic value.

wood. Different woody plants have characteristic cell structures and grain that can lead to identification down to the genus level—such as spruce, oak, pine, or maple—even with small samples.

- This type of identification can't usually go down to the species level, though, the way it can with pollen, flowers, or leaves. So far, DNA testing is not possible with wood because there are only minute quantities of DNA contained in wood.

- Some wooden objects that could be involved in crimes are cultural artifacts or prized antiques that may need authentication by a wood expert, and some types of trees are protected species and are illegal to harvest, but there are also crimes against people that require forensic wood identification or the linking of pieces of wood by examining fracture patterns and other clues.

- The Lindbergh kidnapping is a famous example of a case that used wood matching as critical evidence to identify a carpenter named Bruno Hauptman as the man who abducted and murdered the infant son of Charles Lindbergh, who was the first man to fly solo across the Atlantic Ocean.

Analyzing Animal Evidence

- Some types of forensic investigators specialize in identifying animal abuse and ensuring animal safety to try to guarantee that domesticated animals are treated humanely, and when forensic evidence suggests otherwise, charges may be brought against the perpetrators.

- A relatively recent branch of forensic science called wildlife forensics has a few main focuses: Forensic wildlife investigators examine poaching violations and help protect endangered species—both animals and plants—and they look into the poisoning of wildlife to try to figure out if an event stems from malicious and intentional baiting of animals or is an accident.

- As a science, wildlife forensics emerged out of the U.S. Endangered Species Act of 1973 and the UN Convention of International Trade in Endangered Species, which is comprised of 175 member parties that have agreed to be legally bound by its guidelines in order to protect our natural world.

- In terms of criminal activity, the illegal trade of international wildlife is third only to drugs and guns and affects hundreds of millions of plant and animal species. Some of the problem is that cultural customs, understanding of ecology, and environmental awareness vary significantly around the world.

- One of the problems with investigating various poaching violations—as well as other forms of illegal collection of plant and animal products—is that the evidence rarely involves whole plants or whole animals, which can be easily identified by zoo, museum, and botanical experts.

- Some animal violations have to be detected by examining food products, such as fresh, frozen, or smoked meats. Other animal evidence comes in the form of commercial or handmade products that are made from protected species. Some animal and plant materials can be significantly altered—ground up, dried, or crushed—sometimes making them even more difficult to identify.

- Although wildlife forensics deals with many different species as compared to traditional forensics, it still involves many of the same experts. In addition, however, mammalian osteologists examine teeth, bones, and antlers to see if age requirements for hunting have been met, and they can also try to match dismembered body parts. Ornithologists examine feathers and talons as potential evidence of illegal hunting of protected bird species.

- Out of a need to enforce established laws and protect our natural world and the creatures in it, the U.S. Fish and Wildlife Service Forensics Laboratory was founded in 1988. This high-tech crime lab and its team of experts perform a large number of forensic examinations covering all parts of the United States.

- In the United States, the entity that governs the trade of animal and plant products, including their import and export, is the Department of Homeland Security. The regulations that are enforced through the Customs and Border Protection division are important not only for the preservation of endangered species, but also to protect our environment from the introduction of nonnative species that could harm U.S. ecosystems.

Analyzing Environmental Damage and Contamination

- Abnormal odors, areas called dead zones in plant growth, and dead fish in waterways can all be clues that something or someone could be poisoning the environment. Whether the toxicity is due to an intentional release of chemicals or is accidental contamination, these types of incidents need to be investigated and often culminate in criminal and/or civil litigation.

- Commonly encountered poisons include heavy metals, different types of insecticides, toxins intended to kill rodents, and even barbiturates that can leach into the environment when the carcasses of euthanized animals are dumped into landfills. Sometimes, the patterns in the dead animals can reveal the particular toxin involved.

- The forensic identification of pesticides and other toxic chemicals in the environment is critical because not only does it damage plant and animal life, but it can also harm and kill humans. Because plants and animals are lower on the food chain, they are often the first indicators of environmental damage. When wildlife investigators pick up on these clues, the work they do might ultimately protect human health.

- Even if rehabilitation groups step in to help sick or injured animals after an oil spill or other toxic event, important documentation—such as photos, carcasses, tissue samples, and even feces and vomit—has to be kept because of its eventual importance if there is ever a trial.

When Animals Attack Humans

- When people travel to or live in relatively remote places, there's an increased likelihood that they will encounter potentially dangerous wildlife. Sometimes, diseased animals—such as those with rabies—lose their fear and enter areas they normally wouldn't.

- Fatal attacks by animals to humans must be reported to the governing coroner or medical examiner—just as with any other unexpected death. Even when someone survives an animal attack, the proper authorities should be notified, and any necessary media releases should be made through the proper channels, especially if the animal is still at large.

- When animals attack, the bites they leave on a victim can be examined using the same type of bite-mark analyses that forensic odontologists use when people bite each other. Bite-mark analysis can be used to help identify the type of critter involved in an animal attack and possibly even to tie the victim to a specific animal, if it's found.

- When investigators have to search for an animal at large, they use the same types of strategies as when searching for a human predator, but they track for paws, fur, and scat (animal feces). If necessary, paw prints can be cast using the same types of methods that are used with shoe and tire impressions.

- If the suspect animal is caught, it may have to be analyzed to see if it is, in fact, the perpetrator. This is usually done by examining the animal's stomach contents.

Suggested Reading

Gunn, *Essential Forensic Biology*.

1. How can soil be used as evidence in a crime?

2. What are protists, and where might they be found?

3. What types of plant materials constitute crime-scene evidence?

4. How are animals used in forensic science?

5. Can environmental contamination be a criminal act?

Serology—Blood and Other Body Fluids
Lecture 9

Violent crimes are the most likely to produce body fluid evidence, consisting primarily of blood and semen from rapes or other physical attacks, but the science of body fluids—known as serology—can be applied to many other substances, such as saliva, sweat, tears, vomit, and vaginal secretions. The difficulty with analyzing body fluids at crime scenes is that the perpetrator often does everything in his or her power to clean up the scene—at least on the surface.

Detecting Body Fluids at Crime Scenes

- If body fluids are suspected at a crime scene, the investigator has to consider several questions: What type of body fluids might be present? What state is the fluid in—liquid or dried? Is it fresh or degraded? These factors impact how the substance can be collected and analyzed. The next major consideration is whether the fluid came from a human or some other animal.

- The science of serology can be used to answer all of those questions, and some can even be answered at the crime scene. Serology can even automatically exclude a person as a suspect—just as with hair. However, just as with hair evidence, serology cannot tie a body fluid to a specific and unique source, which requires DNA testing.

- At some crime scenes, the presence of blood or other body fluids might be obvious, but in other cases, investigators might not see clear signs that blood is present. In order to determine whether or not blood is present, there are a few types of presumptive tests that can be done at the crime scene.

- A presumptive test is a quick way to figure out the likelihood of whether something is what you think it is in the field. With regard to serology, presumptive testing helps investigators figure out where blood and other body fluids might be, which will help them determine what might have happened and what to collect.

- Some presumptive tests occasionally produce a false positive result, so these types of tests always have to be followed up in a forensic lab with confirmatory tests, which are much more reliable and discriminatory—but also take more time and cost much more money.

- Luminol is the presumptive test that is most often used in cases where the perpetrator has tried to clean up the scene because luminol can detect blood in minute quantities by spraying it and turning off the lights. Unfortunately, it doesn't work if chlorine bleach was used to clean up blood. However, you can use it in the field and it doesn't completely ruin the blood for further testing.

- On television shows, investigators spray what looks like a clean wall with a phony chemical, but when they turn out the lights, there are a bunch of spots—a blood spatter pattern—not a cleaning smear with wipe marks, which is what is seen in reality.

- There are some other presumptive tests, specifically for blood, that use chemistry to produce a color change. The most commonly used test is the Kastle-Meyer test, which detects the hemoglobin in red blood cells.

Human Blood Typing and Immunology
- Austrian physician Karl Landsteiner discovered how to type blood in 1901. In 1925, it was discovered that about 80% of the human population secretes a variety of proteins native to their blood in their tears, saliva, sweat, urine, and semen—making it possible to test some nonblood body fluids and still determine a person's blood type in the majority of cases.

- The 2 main protein systems that are typically used to determine human blood type are the ABO system and the Rh protein. These 2 proteins are both found in human red blood cells. The Rh protein isn't used in forensic science—it's mainly used in blood tests for compatibility—but the ABO system is.

- The cell membranes of red blood cells have proteins known as antigens on them, and they come in 2 forms: A and B. If someone has type-A blood, their red blood cells have the A form of the protein antigen; if they have type-B blood, their red blood cells have the B-protein antigen. If a person has type-AB blood, they express both the A and B forms of the proteins, and if they have type-O blood, they express no proteins for this particular blood system.

- Immunology is the study of the interactions between the 2 major groups of genetically determined biological proteins known as antigens and antibodies. An antigen is anything that the body reacts to by producing an antibody. Antibodies are proteins that our immune system can make to fight a specific intruder.

- Normally, we develop antibodies through vaccines or by encounters we have with foreign substances in the environment—such as when we get sick—but in the strange case of the ABO blood system, we are born with genetically determined antibodies in the liquid part of our blood known as plasma. We have antibodies to the opposing types of red blood cells that we might encounter.

- Our antibodies attack and attach to foreign antigens in order to deactivate them, and the antibodies we make are specific to the antigens they encounter in a one-to-one relationship. Serologists target the original blood sample with a solution of antibodies and let the antibodies reveal what antigens are present because those antigens determine blood type.

Applications of Blood Typing
- Blood can be found at a crime scene in many different forms. It can be relatively fresh, or it can be dried up. In fact, all items of evidence that have blood on them are dried by the time they reach the forensic lab because blood is more stable when it's dry.

- Blood typing in a forensic lab is often very different from the standard blood typing done in a hospital lab because forensic scientists are typically dealing with blood and other body fluids that are degraded, old, contaminated, and sometimes commingled.

- Figuring out whether blood is from a human and not an animal requires the use of antibodies that are specific to antigens only found in human blood. Forensic labs have commercially prepared stock solutions of antibodies to the blood of many common animals that are typical pets or those we eat.

- A person's blood type is genetically inherited, and before DNA technology, blood types were used routinely in paternity tests.

Dried blood—on a knife, for example—resists bacterial growth better and is much more stable than liquid blood.

- Human red blood cell typing can only exclude or include someone as being a suspect; it cannot show that the blood in question came from a specific person. In other words, blood type is class evidence—not individuating evidence.

- There are different distributions of the ABO blood groups in different human populations. The long-standing genetic isolation of major ancestral or racial groups has led to some blood types being more common in some groups over others.

Fluids Other Than Blood
- In addition to blood, the science of serology also deals with other body fluids. Saliva, semen, and vaginal fluid may also be exchanged between perpetrators and their victims in sexual assaults. The testing for these types of fluids is similar to blood; there are presumptive tests that can be done in the field and then confirmatory tests that are done later in the lab.

65

- One presumptive test for semen involves looking for a chemical known as acid phosphatase, a chemical made by the male reproductive glands known as the seminal vesicles. Those glands produce the bulk of the fluid portion of semen.

- The problem with acid phosphatase is that it's fairly common in nature, including being present in the body fluids of nonhuman animals. Confirmatory tests for semen include a microscopic exam to look for sperm cells, which can still be detected even if the sperm are dead and starting to degrade.

- If the rapist had a vasectomy, looking for sperm would be useless. Fortunately, though, seminal acid phosphatase levels are not affected by a vastectomy and neither is the chemical prostate-specific antigen (PSA), which is considered a confirmatory test for the presence of semen because unlike acid phosphatase, it is unique to semen.

- Timing is important in serology cases involving sexual assault. If a woman is raped and murdered, the medical examiner may find evidence of sperm in her vagina for up to about 2 weeks, but in a living victim, live sperm will only be found for about 5 hours after a rape occurred, and after about 72 hours, there may be no remaining evidence of sperm or semen.

From Professor Murray's Forensic Files

I was once involved in a case where a man in the military was caught on duty on base cheating on his 8-month-pregnant wife with one of his female subordinate officers. He was immediately dismissed from duty and was facing a court-martial procedure.

When he didn't come home for a few days, his wife flew to her mother's house until the baby was born. A few weeks later, the man's truck was located in a wooded area, which prompted a search. Down a rocky ravine, his decomposing body was found along with a bottle of whiskey and a shotgun.

The man's skull was in about 65 pieces, and the medical examiner wanted me to try to reconstruct the skull to make sure this was, in fact, a suicide as they suspected. After I glued the skull back together, I was able to see that there was a close-contact gunshot wound to the temple—not the forehead. I also saw gunshot residue on the bone, suggesting that this man had been shot at close range from the side.

It's possible for a full-grown man to hold a shotgun out to the side of his head and shoot himself, depending on the length of his arm, but this man wasn't very large, and the typical length of a shotgun barrel is 24 to 34 inches. Furthermore, that's an awkward direction to generate the kind of force needed to pull the trigger.

The police called the man's wife and got access to search their home with her permission, but nothing seemed out of place. Then, one of the cops decided to fly out to the mother's house to speak more directly with her. Within a few minutes of questioning, the man's pregnant widow crumbled and told the officer that she had shot her husband in their bed on the night she heard about his affair.

The cops went back to the couple's house and used luminol in the bedroom, where they found evidence of blood on the headboard, the wall, and the carpeting—but not on the mattress. Even though the surfaces looked clean to the unaided eye, when luminol was sprayed and the lights were turned off, the bloodstains become immediately visible.

They later found the full-sized bloody mattress the wife had dumped in a different location. Incidentally, the wife was found not guilty after using the battered wife defense on a sympathetic jury.

Gaensslen, *Sourcebook in Forensic Serology, Immunology, and Biochemistry*.

Questions to Consider

1. What types of body fluids can be found at a crime scene?

2. What values do the analyses of body fluids have—other than the DNA evidence they contain?

3. How do investigators sample body fluids from a crime scene?

4. What is the difference between a presumptive test and a confirmatory test?

5. Do the same types of body fluids need to be compared—blood with blood, for example—to get a conclusive match between a suspect and crime-scene evidence?

The Forensic Analysis of DNA
Lecture 10

D NA evidence is similar to other kinds of evidence in the way that it relies on comparisons between samples taken from people—whether the samples are from known or unknown persons or from the crime scene. Unlike hair and serology, however, DNA is one of the rare pieces of evidence that can be statistically linked to a single person at the exclusion of all others, and because DNA can be found in all body tissues and fluids, it has even greater identification potential than fingerprints.

Using DNA Evidence to Convict and Exonerate

- In England in 1983, the body of a 15-year-old girl named Lynda Mann was found. She had been raped, strangled, and left on a path in the woods. After a semen stain was found on her clothes, investigators at the UK's Forensic Science Service performed a standard serology exam and discovered that the semen came from a man with type-A blood. They also did an enzyme analysis, which showed a protein pattern that would likely match about 10% of the male population.

- Almost 3 years later in the same county, another 15-year-old girl named Dawn Ashworth was found raped and strangled in the woods. A serology exam showed that the blood type and enzyme profile from the semen was the same as the 1983 case. Police honed in on a 17-year-old boy named Richard Buckland, who admitted to killing Dawn Ashworth but denied having anything to do with the 1983 murder of Lynda Mann.

- At nearby Leicester University, a professor named Dr. Alec Jeffreys had figured out that there were some repeated sequences in the genetic code of DNA that varied from person to person. With the semen samples from the 2 murders and the DNA from the confessed killer, Jeffreys discovered that the DNA profile from the semen on the 2 girls was identical—but it didn't match up to Buckland.

- Then, the police asked every 17- to 34-year-old man in the county to give them a blood and saliva sample. After analyzing about 5000 samples, they found no match. Eventually, a woman contacted police because she overheard a friend saying that he was paid 200 pounds to submit a sample in the name of Colin Pitchfork.

- When the cops found Pitchfork, his DNA matched the semen from both of the murder victims. Not only was this the first case of conviction through DNA evidence, but it was also the first case of exoneration because Buckland was shown not to have been the murderer—despite his false confession.

The DNA Molecule

- Deoxyribonucleic acid (DNA) is the genetic molecule that makes up our chromosomes and encodes the instructions for when and how to make proteins in a living organism. All standard cells have DNA—from bacterial cells to the cells of the most complicated creatures.

- The DNA molecule is like a twisted ladder, where the sides of the ladder are made out of phosphates and sugars and the rungs of the ladder are made out of pairs of smaller molecules called nucleotides.

- In spite of all the genetic diversity on Earth, the alphabet that makes up the genetic code of all living things has only 4 letters: A, C, G, and T.

- Living things are more similar when they share more of their genetic code in common and less similar when they don't. Humans share about 97% of our genes with our closest living relatives, chimpanzees.

- It's estimated that human beings differ from one another by less than 1% of our DNA because most of it is devoted to making basic body structures and controlling standard functions—with only a little variability related to family history.

- When DNA differs in a group like humans, the difference is known as a polymorphism, a term that means having many forms. There are 2 kinds of polymorphisms in human genes: a sequence polymorphism, in which there's a difference in the order of the nucleotide base pairs in a stretch of DNA, and length polymorphism, in which a phrase in the genetic code gets repeated a number of times.

- Scientists have figured out some of the more standard genetic repeats and call them variable number tandem repeats (VNTRs), which are used to categorize, or type, DNA.

- When scientists look at multiple stretches of DNA at the same time between 2 people, the statistical probabilities that any 2 people could have the same VNTR pattern by coincidence become strong enough to let genetic comparisons link a single person to a DNA profile—at the exclusion of anyone else, except an identical twin.

DNA and Inheritance

- We have 2 types of DNA in our cells: Nuclear DNA is located inside the nucleus of our cells, and mitochondrial DNA is located inside the small energy-producing organelles called mitochondria that are in our cells.

- Nuclear DNA is the double-stranded, twisted-ladder molecule. Within the nucleus of our cells, it's packaged into units called chromosomes. Nuclear DNA is inherited from both of our parents; we get 23 chromosomes of DNA from our father and 23 chromosomes of DNA from our mother at our conception. Through the interaction of dominant and recessive genes, nuclear DNA gives us the traits that make us who we are biologically.

- Every cell in your body contains the same nuclear DNA—which is important to forensics—and each cell in your body has only one copy of your nuclear DNA. In addition, we each have a unique set of nuclear DNA that belongs to nobody else in the world unless we have an identical twin.

- Because we each only get 1/2 of our mom's chromosomes and 1/2 of our dad's chromosomes, we share some of our DNA with them but not all. The closer we are related to people, the more nuclear DNA we share in common with them.

- Mitochondrial DNA is inherited completely from our mother. Because of this, we share 100% mitochondrial DNA identity with her—and not only with her, but also with every other child she has—and the same mitochondrial DNA is found in all of our mother's siblings.

DNA and Forensic Science

- Long before DNA was used in forensics, scientists knew it could be found in body cells, so any source of living or dead cells—as long as the cells aren't too badly degraded—is a potential source of either nuclear or mitochondrial DNA.

- Lots of early forensic DNA research involved trying to figure out the best sources of crime-scene DNA. Blood, semen, and other body tissues are obvious sources, but eventually scientists figured out that DNA is left behind on things like cigarette butts, licked envelope seals, hair follicles, and latex gloves.

- Biological evidence is perishable, and even though DNA is a durable molecule, it will degrade over time and fragment. In general, fresh tissues yield more nuclear DNA than older tissues, but when a nuclear DNA profile isn't possible, analysts may still be able to get mitochondrial DNA out of an old sample.

- At a crime scene, possible sources of DNA have to be handled carefully. Anything wet, such as a piece of cloth with blood on it, should be air-dried and put into a container that is open a little to stop moisture buildup. It also should be kept at a low temperature—or at least nothing higher than room temperature—to help prevent the growth of bacteria and fungi, which have their own DNA.

- Sometimes, you can't avoid environmental contamination, such as when a body decomposes in a lake or some other body of water. Once the body is in the morgue, DNA analysts can figure out how to minimize cross-contamination with the many creatures that live in bodies of water.

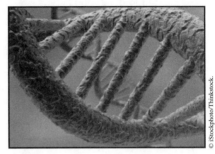

DNA is one of the oldest biologically active molecules on the planet.

- If the DNA sample is on a surface that is portable—such as a coffee mug or a piece of chewed gum—then the whole thing should be sent to the lab. However, if the whole thing isn't easily transported, then a sample that contains the questioned DNA can be taken from it.

- Evidence technicians not only have to be careful with samples to preserve the DNA in them, but they also have to think about their own safety because body fluids can carry infections. Scene and lab workers also have to make sure that they don't contaminate crime-scene evidence with their own DNA from their hair, dandruff, skin cells, or saliva.

- When investigators need a known sample from a particular person to compare to unknown crime-scene samples, they can use blood, but most often, known samples—called reference samples—are taken with a buccal swab, which is a sterile cotton swab that is rubbed over the inside of someone's cheek and then put into an envelope.

- In the morgue, DNA samples are often taken from unknown persons to help get them identified. If investigators have a pretty good idea of who they think the victim is, then they can find relatives to take reference samples from for comparison, but if no relatives are available, then a reference sample might come from the victim—in the form of a toothbrush or stored medical tissues, such as donated blood in a blood bank.

DNA Profiling
- At the lab, DNA scientists can extract genetic material from crime-scene or reference samples. To find and capitalize on the tiny fractions of DNA that differ among people—rather than the over 99% of our DNA that we have in common—scientists use sequence and length polymorphisms to develop someone's DNA profile, or DNA fingerprint.

- The first successful method of DNA profiling was restriction fragment length polymorphism (RFLP) analysis, which uses a restriction enzyme to cut DNA at polymorphic places to create DNA fragments that differ between 2 people. After using gel electrophoresis, which sorts the RFLP fragments by size, the resulting DNA fingerprint can be compared to other DNA samples.

- RFLP is problematic because it requires a fairly large sample, and the results aren't compatible with the major DNA computer databases.

- In 1983, a technique for mass-producing copies of DNA was developed called polymerase chain reaction (PCR), which amplifies a small sample of DNA so that there's plenty of it to analyze in a forensic case.

- RFLP typing of DNA has been replaced by short tandem repeat (STR) analysis, which uses PCR and some of the same principles as RFLP but is quicker and doesn't require as much sample DNA.

- The profiles generated by STR are sets of numbers that can be entered into the combined DNA index system (CODIS) database, which lets agencies easily compare the DNA profiles they obtain to those from other cases—and even to missing persons and offender databases.

- Another advance in DNA technology is the fairly recent ability to tell whether a sample is from a woman or a man by looking at DNA from the sex chromosomes.

Suggested Reading

Butler, *Advanced Topics in Forensic DNA Typing.*

———, *Fundamentals of Forensic DNA Typing.*

Hunter, *DNA Analysis.*

Questions to Consider

1. About how long has DNA analysis been a part of forensic science?

2. What is the difference between nuclear DNA and mitochondrial DNA?

3. How do we inherit the 2 different types of DNA within our cells?

4. Is nuclear DNA or mitochondrial DNA more unique?

Forensic Toxicology of Drugs and Poisons
Lecture 11

F orensic labs examine a variety of body fluids and tissues to extract and analyze the DNA molecule—which, of course, is native to our cells— but there are many other types of tests that are conducted in forensic labs to look for chemicals or drugs that are introduced into our bodies. Toxicology is the study of how animals, including humans, are affected by drugs and poisonous substances. The science of forensic toxicology is important because many drug and poison issues have legal ramifications.

Forensic Chemistry and Toxicology Labs

- Many forensic labs have 2 chemistry sections within them: a forensic chemistry lab that analyzes contraband, abused substances in dosage or seized form, and a toxicology lab that looks for drugs or other chemicals in biological samples such as urine, blood, or other body tissues—in other words, after people have a chemical in their system.

- The reason that there are 2 chemistry sections in forensic labs has to do with the huge differences in concentrations between a drug on the street and a drug in someone's body. The forensic chemistry lab analyzes grams and kilograms of drugs, but the toxicology lab looks for drugs in nanogram and microgram amounts.

- These 2 sides of forensics use different supplies and different analytical instruments housed in separate locations because of the potential for cross-contamination that would taint drug and poison results in the toxicology lab.

- A drug is a single chemical, or mix of chemicals, that has psychological and/or physiological effects on the body. Therapeutic drugs—such as aspirin and antibiotics—are taken for various ailments while other drugs are recreational. Some, such as alcohol and caffeine, are legal while others are not.

- Many drugs or chemicals that are typically innocuous—or even helpful to the body—can be toxic in excess. This is even true for substances normally found in the body, such as the hormone insulin, which will lower blood sugar to the point of death if given in high enough dosage.

- A poison is something that has life-threatening effects, which are often collectively known as toxicity. Both legal and illegal drugs can be poisonous if not taken in the right amounts or if taken in combination with other substances. Legal drugs and even prescription drugs can also have unanticipated toxic side effects that might affect some individuals—even when those drugs are taken properly.

The Science of Pharmacokinetics

- The way drugs act in the body and the effects they have on the body are studied within the science of pharmacology, which can be broken down into 2 areas: pharmacokinetics and pharmacodynamics.

- Pharmacokinetics is the study of the way drugs move—including how they get into and out of the body—which can be organized into 4 main areas: absorption, distribution, metabolism, and elimination.

- Although drugs can enter the body in a variety of ways, blood is the superhighway that drugs use once they're inside. Most drugs don't affect people indefinitely because they're metabolized, after which most drugs—but not all—are removed from the body in a few different ways.

- Absorption is how a drug gets into the body. Drugs can be injected directly into the blood intravenously—which means right into a vein—or injected into a muscle or under the skin where they'll enter the blood a little more gradually. Drugs can also be introduced orally or rectally, where they'll have to cross the mucous membrane lining of the gastrointestinal tract to reach the bloodstream.

- Some drugs enter the extensive network of blood vessels of the lungs by being inhaled while others can cross the skin by being applied topically. Some drugs, especially those used on the skin to treat the skin—including some anesthetics—might not end up in significant levels in the circulatory system, so they are said to act more locally.

- In terms of distribution, if a drug is not intended to act only locally, it's the circulating blood that carries the drug to almost all parts of the body. Depending on the size or chemistry of the drug, it may not reach all parts of the body. Therefore, when a person takes a drug, it may end up at different concentrations in different parts of the body.

- Metabolism is the way in which a drug is broken down within the body into other substances, which can be called metabolites, and usually takes place in the liver. Sometimes, there are multiple steps in the process of metabolism for a given drug so that even metabolites can be further broken down into other chemicals in a series of body reactions.

- The breakdown of a drug has 4 main possible outcomes.

  o First, it deactivates the drug, which ultimately limits or lessens its effects on the body.

  o Second, metabolism of a drug usually makes it easier for the body to get rid of it because metabolites are smaller and usually more water soluble than the parent drug they come from.

  o Third, metabolism can convert the drug into a substance that's usable for energy.

  o Fourth, a parent drug can be metabolized to the active drug.

- The final step in pharmacokinetics is elimination. Most drugs leave the body in urine because the bloodstream carries them to the kidneys, where blood is filtered. This puts the drug and/or its metabolites into urine, which is why most drug tests involve urine testing.

- Other drugs and/or metabolites can exit the body in feces and sweat, through respiration when people exhale, by being deposited in hair that is growing in a follicle, or through lactation in nursing mothers. These are all sources of forensic testing.

The Science of Pharmacodynamics

- The reason that a drug can exert an effect on the body is because drugs and other substances, such as our body's hormones, are like chemical keys. The locks that those keys may fit are called receptors, which are some of the many types of proteins found on the surface of cells. There are even some types of receptors that are inside of cells.

- Even though a drug may be coursing through the bloodstream, the only cells that are targets for that drug are those that have the matching receptors for it, and when a drug key finds one of its matching receptor locks, it will bind to that receptor, and in turn, the cell will react in some way.

- There are 2 main ways drugs interact with cells in the body: Some drugs chemically tell a cell to perform a certain function when they bind to a receptor on that cell, and some drugs interact with other drugs, which is known as synergism—when 2 or more drugs are taken together, they sometimes have a greater effect than either would have if taken individually.

- The science of pharmacodynamics also has allowed an understanding of drug dependence and drug addiction, which are not the same.

- Dependence is a psychological need for a certain drug; if a person stops taking that drug, he or she does not have physical symptoms of withdrawal.

- When someone is addicted to a drug, his or her body physically needs the drug to continue functioning. If the addicted person stops taking the drug, he or she goes into withdrawal, which can include symptoms such as high temperature, pain, seizures, and even death.

- The phenomenon of tolerance occurs when the body adapts to a drug. As tolerance builds up, increasingly higher quantities of the drug need to be taken to achieve the same effects. Tolerance occurs with most drugs to some degree—even with some prescription drugs—but tolerance is especially pronounced for substances such as morphine, heroin, cocaine, alcohol, and barbiturates.

- Reverse tolerance, or sensitization, occurs when users experience heightened effects from the same dose of a drug, which can occur with stimulants such as methamphetamine or cocaine.

Forensic Drug Testing
- Forensic drug testing can be divided into 2 main areas: testing on the living and testing on the dead. Tests on living people involve looking for illegal, banned, or abused substances. Reasons for drug tests on the living include preemployment drug tests and random drug tests to help ensure public safety or to make sure that athletes compete fairly.

- The postmortem forensic drug testing of body fluids and body tissues involves poisoning cases, which can be accidental, suicidal, or homicidal. When looking for and at toxicity, forensic toxicologists work in conjunction with forensic pathologists, who are medical doctors that specialize in the study of disease and trauma in the morgue.

- In order for toxicologists to discover whether a poisoning was accidental or intentional, they need to take a number of things into account. If possible, this includes getting personal information about the victim from family members or medical professionals. Forensic toxicologists can use that information in conjunction with instrumental tests that are run on body fluids and tissues and possibly by testing substances found at the scene that may relate to the incident.

- In a living person, signs of poisoning may include nausea, vomiting, respiratory issues, abnormal coloration of the skin, mental confusion, seizures, and—when severe enough—loss of consciousness. The effects depend on the type of drug involved and the amount and duration of exposure.

- In order to identify one or more drugs in a victim's body, there are 4 main steps: sampling, screening, extraction, and confirmation.

- In sampling, body fluids and/or tissues are taken from the victim to search for drugs or other chemicals. In antemortem testing, the choice of the sample is determined by what the lab thinks it is looking for or how long the drug or chemical has been in the body.

- The most typical samples for antemortem drug testing are blood and urine. In postmortem testing, in addition to blood and urine, vitreous fluid from the eye, stomach contents, bile, brain, and liver tissue are commonly collected.

- Once the toxicology lab has obtained samples, screening tests are conducted that are similar to presumptive tests—except they're done in the lab. These preliminary tests indicate that a drug may be present, which then

In poisoning cases, postmortem forensic drug testing can be done to analyze body fluids and body tissues.

allows the toxicologist to know what direction to go in for further testing.

- Screening tests can sometimes be problematic because some drugs mimic naturally occurring substances, and vice versa. Examples of common toxicology screening tests include gas chromatography and enzyme-multiplied immunoassay testing.

- Then, the toxicologist needs to extract the drugs for confirmatory testing. The purposes of extraction are to clean up the drug so that there aren't other substances present that could contaminate the testing instruments and to concentrate the drug so that it will be easier to detect. The extraction method that is chosen depends on the drug and the body fluid or tissue sample being used.

- When investigators need to know precisely what substances are in a mixture and in exactly what quantities, the current state-of-the-art confirmatory test for most chemicals and drugs is mass spectrometry, which can be calibrated with known standards to measure a drug's quantity in a sample.

Suggested Reading

Trestrail, *Criminal Poisoning*.

Questions to Consider

1. What is toxicology?

2. What is the difference between a drug and a poison?

3. What different types of forensic cases might involve toxicology testing?

4. What are some sources of tissues or body fluids that can be used for drug and poison testing?

The Forensics of Substance Abuse
Lecture 12

It's difficult to find accurate statistics for substance-abuse deaths because the problem is so insidious and so intertwined with deaths from other causes, such as alcohol-related traffic accidents and drug-related criminal acts. In addition, deaths are just the tip of the iceberg in forensic substance-abuse issues. By far, the largest part of the day-to-day operations in crime labs is the chemical testing of contraband substances that are potentially illegal drugs. In fact, drug evidence accounts for more than 50% of all the evidence that ends up in forensic labs—including fingerprints, hair, fibers, and blood.

The Forensics of Substance Abuse
- In general, drugs of abuse can be classified into 4 major categories by source.

    o First, some come from naturally occurring plant and fungal origins and are smoked or ingested in basically their original form, such as marijuana, peyote buttons, and some mushrooms.

    o Secondly, some drugs of abuse are extracted from plants, such as cocaine, morphine, and codeine.

    o A third classification is semisynthetic drugs that are manufactured from a naturally occurring substance, such as heroin or LSD.

    o The fourth category of abused drugs is synthetics, which are entirely man-made, such as barbiturates, amphetamines, and oxycodone.

- Drugs are more commonly classified by the effects they typically have on those who take them, such as depressants, stimulants, narcotics, and hallucinogens. Despite common belief, alcohol is a depressant, and marijuana is a hallucinogen.

Depressants

- Depressants, which are often called sedatives in low doses, are drugs that generally decrease brain activity, reduce muscle activity, lower respiration and heart rate, induce sleep, and reduce anxiety—sometimes to the point of mild euphoria.

- Overdoses of depressants kill people by paralyzing the respiratory center in their brain, and when people are addicted to these types of depressants, a sudden withdrawal can be lethal as well. Street names include downers and barbs—which is short for barbiturates, the most common class of depressants in the United States.

- Benzodiazepines and related drugs make up a large family of synthetic depressants, which are especially known for their antianxiety and sleep-inducing effects. Many of these have familiar brand names, such as Xanax, Klonopin, and Ativan.

Stimulants

- Stimulants are drugs that are known to elevate mood, reduce depression, raise blood pressure, elevate heart and respiration rates, and produce intense euphoria and energy. Caffeine is a common and unregulated stimulant, but some illicit and very dangerous stimulants have been manufactured from relatively benign substances—such as lithium—in clandestine labs, such as meth labs.

- The class of stimulants known as amphetamines was originally developed to relieve the symptoms of asthma and hay fever but went on to be used to treat narcolepsy or hyperactivity and to suppress appetite. Adderall and Dexedrine are a few familiar brand names.

- Cocaine is a stimulant that resembles amphetamine in its potential for abuse and its pharmacology. Cocaine is extracted from the coca leaf grown in the Andes Mountains. It is extracted with hydrochloric acid to form the compound cocaine hydrochloride and is also known by the street names snow, flake, and blow. When cocaine hydrochloride is treated with a base and extracted into an organic solvent, it forms freebase, or crack, cocaine, which can be smoked, resulting in a greater effect but also in an increase in the chance of death.

Narcotics

- The term "narcotic" is a catchall for many drugs that are considered highly dangerous. Narcotics are still used legally as painkillers and sleeping aids. The opium resin from the poppy plant has been used traditionally for over 5000 years to relieve pain, to decrease diarrhea, and as a recreational drug in many cultures.

- Codeine has long been used in cough suppressants—and mixed with aspirin, or more recently with acetaminophen, which is Tylenol—to boost their pain-management capabilities. Morphine also has a long history as an analgesic and is still used to control pain, in particular after surgery. Heroin is derived from morphine but is about 10 times more potent; it's used as a painkiller in some other countries but not in the United States.

- Methadone is a synthetic opiate substitute used in the United States to help wean addicts off of heroin under medical supervision. There are many other narcotics used as pain relievers today that are frequently abused and illegally trafficked. This includes a large group of synthetic and semisynthetic compounds, such as Dilaudid, Vicodin, Lortab, and Demerol.

- Oxycodone is a narcotic that has been put in a time-released form called OxyContin or combined with aspirin in Percodan or with acetaminophen in Percocet. Fentanyl is another narcotic that is about 100 times more potent than morphine.

Hallucinogens

- The fourth class of typically abused drugs is hallucinogens, but these have no accepted medical uses in the United States, with the recent exception of some states allowing medicinal marijuana usage. Hallucinogens have perception-altering effects and include 4 subcategories: psychedelics, deliriants, disassociatives, and cannabinoids—each with slightly different mind-bending properties.

- Psychedelics, the classical hallucinogens, include semisynthetics, such as lysergic acid diethylamide (LSD), and naturally occurring mescaline and psilocybin mushrooms. A huge problem with psilocybin abuse is the extra risk of poisoning because people mistakenly ingest toxic lookalike mushrooms and die.

- The deliriant forms of hallucinogens are also called true hallucinogens because people taking them will have conversations with people who aren't there, for example. Deliriants are part of a group of compounds known as anticholinergics because of their effects on the nervous system and include derivatives from mandrake plants as well as MDMA, or ecstasy.

- Phencyclidine, abbreviated PCP and known as angel dust, is a powerful hallucinogen of the dissociative variety. The manic behavior and feelings of strength, power, and invulnerability seen in people on PCP make them formidable opponents for law enforcement. Other dissociatives include ketamine (special K), nitrous oxide (laughing gas), and some derivatives of the salvia plant.

- Cannabinoids are the last class of hallucinogens, but they don't fit neatly into any category. Marijuana has mild analgesic and sedative properties but also causes perceptive alterations, memory impairment, mood swings, euphoria, and hallucinations. Heavy use can promote delusions and paranoia.

The History of Drug Regulation in the United States

- In the late 19th century, there really was no drug control in the United States, but—prompted by an increase in patented medicines, cocaine use, and public reaction to opium smoking by Chinese railroad workers—the Pure Food and Drug Act was passed in 1906.

- This became part of a history of regulating the use of drugs of all kinds and linked drug use to the Treasury Department through taxes. Alcohol prohibition happened at the federal level in 1920 with the 18th Amendment of the U.S. Constitution—followed by the repeal of prohibition in 1933.

- In 1956, the Narcotic Drug Control Act was created, which increased penalties for illicit drug use, including that dealers who sold drugs to minors could face the death penalty. Concurrent with this came the responsibility for controlling any substance that had the potential for abuse by the Food and Drug Administration, expanding the sphere of dangerous drugs beyond only narcotics.

- In 1970, the Comprehensive Controlled Substances Act updated or abolished previous dangerous drug laws. This also moved enforcement from the Treasury Department to the Justice Department and marked the beginning of the Drug Enforcement Administration (DEA). Tobacco and alcohol were excluded from the DEA's jurisdiction and instead are regulated by the Bureau of Alcohol, Tobacco, Firearms, and Explosives.

- Ultimately, the U.S. Congress became responsible for scheduling potentially abused substances by dividing them into 5 groups. Drug scheduling is based on the potential for abuse, addiction, and any legitimate medical value the drug has. The lower the schedule number, the higher the potential for abuse and addiction.

Drugs and Toxicology
- Forensic toxicologists are responsible for trying to determine the identity and quantity of drugs in the body—possibly by looking for drug metabolites. They also have to determine whether there are drug interactions if more than one drug is present. Furthermore, they have to relate all of this—if they can—to the history and patterns of drug abuse by the person involved, including whether dependency or tolerance issues played a role. They have to figure out whether a drug was simply in a person's body or whether it contributed to, or was, the cause of death.

- The most common drugs of abuse that toxicologists see in drug deaths are heroin, morphine, and the opiates—but not marijuana and hallucinogens because people don't die even from overdoses of these drugs.

- Whether toxicology is done after an injury or fatality where substance abuse could be involved or during a preemployment or workplace screening, the most common specimens used are blood and urine. Blood tests are typically used when looking for cannaboids or when alcohol use is suspected. Urine tests are better for other suspected substances, especially those that tend to hang around in the body.

The contraband drug section of forensic labs tests substances that are on the street and being sold.

- Part of the reason that forensic chemists have to analyze, quantify, and identify seized substances is because that's part of the basis for determining what charges will be brought against the suspects involved. In some jurisdictions, a larger amount of drug will mean a harsher punishment, but weight isn't everything.

- Many drugs—especially the closer they get to the street-sale level—are usually "cut" with something else. For most states, the total weight of the drug plus the cutting agents count toward the penalty determination. In some states, in the case of small amounts of a drug, there needs to be a usable quantity of the drug—more than a trace—to officially break the law.

- Some forms of the same drug have harsher penalties than another. For example, the U.S. federal government gives out worse punishments for crack cocaine as compared with an equal amount of flake cocaine, so toxicologists have to determine which version it is.

- At the state level, most states don't require impurities to be identified, but in federal cases, cutting agents are identified for intelligence purposes. Knowing what a drug was cut with can make tracing its trafficking and distribution trail easier.

- In the case of large quantities of drugs, sampling is an issue. For example, if a large brick of marijuana comes into the crime lab, analysts will take multiple samples from multiple places on the brick to determine whether the whole package really is marijuana.

- Many of the same toxicological techniques are used to identify potential substances of abuse in the crime lab—such as gas chromatography, mass spectroscopy, and radioimmunoassay. High-performance liquid chromatography (HPLC) and Fourier transformation infrared spectroscopy (FTIR) are also used as confirmatory tests.

- There are also preliminary screening tests available, and some are even used by officers in the field. These can be as simple as looking up the identity of manufactured pills or using quick chemical spot-testing methods. These field tests are sometimes done to be able to get a search warrant, but as with other preliminary tests, they have to be confirmed later by another method.

Questions to Consider

1. About how long have there been governmental drug control entities in the United States?

2. What are the major classes of the typical drugs of abuse?

3. When a huge quantity of a suspected substance is encountered, is every bit of that quantity subject to chemical testing?

Handwriting and Forgery Analysis
Lecture 13

Questioned documents can include anything from a forged check to graffiti scrawled on a wall, and questioned-document experts have just as many techniques for analyzing them. Some, such as handwriting and linguistic analysis, are a bit subjective; others, involving chemical and mechanical analysis, are more objective, but they can also be destructive to the evidence.

What Is a Questioned Document?

- Questioned documents include all sorts of computer-manipulated and hand-altered documents. Questioned-document examiners might look at money, checks, forms, credit cards, stamps, concert and sports tickets, wills, contracts, deeds, ship's logs, passports or other identification, insurance forms, medical records, suicide notes, threatening letters, bank hold up notes, ransom demands, or words written on a wall, a mirror, or even a body at a murder scene.

- Any type of written material could prompt investigation by a questioned-document specialist for both handwriting clues and the materials used to create the document. This includes papers and inks of all sorts; toners used in photocopiers; and print produced by word processors, fax machines, and typewriters.

- Lots of large law-enforcement agencies have document examiners on staff or police officers trained in document analysis. The FBI; the CIA; the Secret Service; the Bureau of Alcohol, Tobacco, Firearms, and Explosives; the Internal Revenue Service; and the U.S. Postal Inspection Service all have questioned-document labs. Military forensic labs and some large private corporations employ document examiners, too.

Handwriting Analysis

- The 2 major areas for questioned-document analysis are handwriting comparisons, which are much more subjective, and materials examination, which are far more objective. Handwriting analysis is not at all the same as graphology—the pseudoscience that alleges you can tell somebody's personality by their handwriting.

- Handwriting analysis involves looking at the class and individual characteristics in a person's writing, usually by comparing the evidence to another writing sample. As we mature in our writing, most of us develop individual characteristics—variations that depend on things like how often we write, how fast we write, and even deliberate changes in style.

- Handwriting also changes with experience, age, and sometimes physical condition. Culturally, styles of cursive writing have changed over time. There may be some minor differences between the handwriting of those who are writing in their native language and a second language as well.

- Casual writing, like a grocery list, might look very different from formal writing, like what you might put on a form in the doctor's office or the address on an envelope. But generally, there are consistencies that mark our handwriting as our own. However, things like someone's sex, race, age, health status, or mental condition cannot be decisively determined from handwriting.

- When a document examiner wants to compare handwriting, a known sample called an exemplar is needed—just as with comparisons of bullets, hair, DNA, and other types of evidence. The more exemplars an examiner has to work with, the better.

- There are times when the examiner might need an exemplar from someone who is no longer alive. Other problems arise when the person providing the exemplar is a suspect in a crime; that person might try to disguise his or her handwriting style.

- There is a standard protocol for obtaining a good requested exemplar: The investigator should make the subject comfortable and provide optimum lighting. The same type of writing instrument and paper should be used as used in the questioned document. The same style of writing should be requested—like print or cursive.

- Most importantly, the writer should have the material dictated for transcription, rather than looking at the questioned document and being asked to copy it. Dictation not only means the writer cannot deliberately try to mismatch the evidence; dictation also tends to make it harder for a person to concentrate solely on the act of writing, making it harder to hide one's natural quirks. For best results, the needed words or phrase should be inserted into some longer passage.

- Features a document examiner would look for include letter size and shape—for example, are they more rounded or tall and thin? Is the handwriting consistently small or large? What about the relative heights of letters? The typical depth below the line of j, g, or y? How about slant? With unlined paper, does the writing tend to creep upward or downward on the page? Finer points include the direction and shape of beginning and end strokes, the letter connections, and quite literally how someone dots i's and crosses t's.

- Pen pressure reveals a lot about a document. Genuine writing shows smooth, rapid, nonstop, free-flowing motions and the absence of any repair and correction strokes. Generally, jerky starts and stops can be signs that someone is trying to duplicate somebody else's handwriting by looking at a copy of it. Fakes include awkward and inconsistent pen movements and inconsistent letter formations throughout as forgers slip back into their own penmanship.

- Analysts cannot always determine who a forger is, since the individual and class characteristics of the forger are not usually present. Investigators can really only say that a document was made by somebody other than the person who wrote the exemplar. Essentially, what investigators are looking for—using no more advanced technology than magnification—are significant similarities or significant differences.

Mechanical Analysis—Typewriters

- Historically, the only printing methods commonly available to people outside the printing industry were typewriters. Although not in common use today in developed countries, document examiners may need to analyze older pieces of writing produced on them.

- Because there were many different kinds of typewriters, examiners have reference files for type styles for different models and manufacturers. From these, they could narrow some fonts down to a specific brand or time period.

- Like other tools, individual typewriters typically had manufacturing defects, like a small notch in a letter's face that would not hit the typewriter ribbon or, conversely, a small bit of extra metal that would give that particular letter a little bump when it appeared on the paper. As a typewriter aged, it could also develop use-wear patterns, like any other tool. The older and less cared-for a typewriter was, the more unique features it would have.

- Next-generation electric typewriters used interchangeable metal spheres, rather than type bars, to strike the ribbon, which meant type could not be traced to an individual machine. It would be impossible for an examiner to get a match between a typewriter and a questioned document unless they were able to locate the exact typewriter ball that was used.

- Investigators had ways to tell if everything on a page was typed at the same time or if, for example, a will had been altered after it was written. Examiners could look for type alignment by using a glass plate with a grid etched on it. They would also compare the ink color—a newly inked ribbon would make darker type than an older ribbon.

Mechanical Analysis—Printers and Photocopiers

- Older dot-matrix printers formed characters by putting down small dots of ink in various patterns. Sometimes, an individual pin could have a defect that might be unique to that machine, but this was not nearly as common as defects on typewriters.

- Ink jet printers, like the name implies, shoot ink onto paper to produce an image or characters. They can sometimes have slight individualizing features, but not often or many. Investigators cannot use fonts to determine printer manufacturers, since many brands have all the same font options. It is thus almost impossible to determine if a document was printed on a specific ink jet printer.

Today's printers and copiers have revolutionized the way documents are produced.

- Laser printers work sort of like photocopiers; the text and images are electronically created on the printer's drum. The toner sticks to the electronic image and is transferred onto the paper. Sometimes it is hard to figure out whether a document was produced on a laser printer or a copier—or if a document is an original from a printer or a photocopy. Like inkjets, you cannot use fonts to determine manufacturer or if a document was printed on a specific printer.

- The machinery that moves paper through a photocopier can sometimes leave small indentations and other marks that can point to a manufacturer. Individual copiers can also have defects that will appear repeatedly on copies; these can link a document to a specific copier—at least until the machine is fixed. Examiners call these trash marks.

- Each time a page is run through a copier, it can pick up new defects, and it is hard to determine whether a questioned document is an original or a copy—or even a copy of a copy. A second-generation photocopy will show the defects of both copiers, and it is nearly impossible to tell which came first.

Mechanical Analysis—Paper

- Questioned-document examiners can also look at the composition and other identifying features of paper. Chemical watermarks are put in after the paper is made, but mechanical watermarks are impressed on the paper during manufacturing and are sometimes coded for quality control. If you have such a mark, not only can the brand be determined, but also when the paper was made.

- Different types of paper vary in how they fluoresce under ultraviolet light and have a variety of fiber types and fiber contents. Two pieces of paper can look identical to the unaided eye, but under the microscope or in the lab they can look or react very differently.

- If somebody tries to insert a new page into a stapled, multipage document like a contract, investigators can look at the staple holes for alignment and the paper type—even its thickness. There are measuring tools called micrometers that can judge the differences in paper thicknesses down to the thousandths of an inch. If a page does not match the rest of a document, that may be suspicious.

- Multiple pages, as in a notebook, can show indented writing. In the movies, a detective will rub the side of a pencil over indented writing; that will not only ruin the paper for fingerprinting, but it can actually smooth out the indentations. Side lighting and photography work much better. An electrostatic device, as used in obtaining shoe prints, is the latest technology for recovering indented writing.

Mechanical Analysis—Ink

- Different inks contain different chemicals, and examiners have all kinds of analytical methods for detecting them, but many chemical tests are destructive, and you cannot just destroy a bunch of evidence to validate your suspicions. Therefore, investigators start with the least damaging methods.

- Ultraviolet and infrared light can show whether any part of the writing on a page was done with different ink. Certain photographic techniques can be useful, too. These types of nondestructive tests can also detect mechanical or chemical erasures. Investigators might not be able to see exactly what was erased, but they can see that something was altered.

- Chemical tests do not always mean destroying a whole page. Examiners can use a hypodermic needle to take a tiny punch out of a piece of inked paper. They can then subject that punch to chromatography and spectrometry tests.

Linguistic Analysis
- Forgeries are common and no doubt as old as writing itself. In fact, during the Middle Ages, a forgery called the Donation of Constantine changed the course of history as we know it. Allegedly written in the 4th century by Constantine the Great, it gave the pope and his successors dominion over all of Italy and the Western Roman Empire, as well as Judea, Greece, Asia, and Africa.

- The document's authenticity was questioned even as early as 1054, but it was officially shown to be a fake in 1440, when Italian humanist Lorenzo Valla exposed it by a detailed linguistic examination—illustrating that because language changes over time, linguistic discrepancies are yet another way forgeries can be exposed.

Suggested Reading

Ellen, *Scientific Examination of Documents*.

Seaman Kelly and Lindblom, *Scientific Examination of Questioned Documents*.

Slyter, *Forensic Signature Examination*.

1. What are some examples of documents that may be of questioned authenticity?

2. Can sex, age, or personality be determined from a handwriting sample by a forensic document examiner?

3. In addition to handwriting analysis, what other types of testing might be done in the analysis of a questioned document?

Computer Forensics and Digital Evidence
Lecture 14

D igital forensics has become an ever-more-important part of crime solving over the past few decades as computers, cell phones, and other electronics become more central to our lives. As crime has moved online, investigators have developed painstaking techniques for retrieving and analyzing digital evidence, which are used side-by-side with traditional police work.

The Age of Digital Crime

- Forensic computer science is concerned with identifying and extracting digital evidence of criminal activity not only from computers but from cell phones, 2-way pagers, cameras, GPS units, fax machines, and all types of other electronic gear. Thus, the current trend is to refer to the analysis of evidence like this as digital forensics.

- Crimes that used to require the perpetrator to commit them in person—or at least required a physical transfer of information (a bank holdup note, a ransom letter)—can now be carried out remotely. Fraud, identity theft, and embezzlement can happen online. Hackers steal corporate data over the Internet. Predators use social networking sites to lure their prey.

- For a digital crime investigation to start, somebody first needs to realize that it has happened. It may take weeks, or even months, before a person or organization becomes aware of a security issue. The initial analysis also has to show that whatever happened is really a criminal act and not a programming glitch or a simple human mistake.

- Next, investigators have to get to the source of the damage and figure out where the incident originated. They must figure out the path the perpetrator used to get to the server or the victim's computer—Was it over the Internet, a wireless network, or by physical means such as attaching a USB drive or inserting a CD into a computer?

- Investigators will also look at the victim to make sure they understand why this person or organization was attacked, which might help them figure out motive. For instance, somebody hacking into a government website might have political motivations. Targeting a single person's bank account would lead investigators down a different path than if the credit card numbers of all consumers doing business with a certain website were stolen.

Digital Forensics Investigations

- A digital forensics analysis team will always include computer experts of some type, but depending on the incident, it might include law enforcement officers who use standard investigative methods out in the community at large, like interviews. Specialists called forensic accountants might be part of the team to look for irregularities in financial records that indicate embezzlement or fraud.

- If the crime was something more like cyber bullying, investigators need to focus on the victim's daily interactions, and they often quickly point a finger at a possible suspect. If the victim has been targeted by a phishing scam, interviewing the victim and figuring out how they may have opened the door to this crime themselves is important.

- The technology itself is used to track down the suspect. The computer experts will start by performing what is called a traceback to find the source computer. In other words, they look for a trail of Internet provider addresses, or IP addresses, that can be followed back to a suspect, or at least a specific computer.

- Meanwhile, the authorities can continue to use routine policing techniques. They might interview the witnesses or check surveillance tapes. If they hone in on a suspect, officers might interview that person's associates to find out what they may know.

- Investigators also look for motive. Some computer security violations are committed simply out of curiosity; we are all familiar with the legends about teenage hackers breaking into government computers for fun. But many, if not most, computer security breaches, Internet scams, and website hacking are done for financial gain. Some digital crimes are committed for power, leverage, revenge, or emotional issues. We must still remember that motive does not equate to guilt.

- Once an investigation has led to a suspect, experts have to figure out whether that person has the knowledge and the means to carry out the digital crime. This is different from many other crimes, because it takes some real know-how to disable serious computer security measures.

- The next step in looking at the suspect is to figure out if they had the access to commit the crime, and this can be also hard to pinpoint. Some viruses have delayed effects or are dependent on certain conditions, such as another program being executed or some other software being run. Smart digital predators can also alter computer logs to give a false picture of when the security breach actually took place.

Digital Chains of Evidence
- To collect, analyze, and preserve digital evidence, authorities need search warrants for the suspect's home computer, work computer, or whatever else could be involved. A search warrant must be specific, and it will set limits on the scope of the examination. If, for example, a warrant is for searching a computer for child pornography, the videotapes in the suspect's home are not covered.

- Laws regulating and governing electronic media and the ability of authorities to monitor and investigate what people do with their digital communication devices include the Cable Communications

Policy Act of 1984, the Electronic Communications Privacy Act of 1986, the Digital Millennium Copyright act of 1998, and the USA Patriot Act of 2001.

• Collecting digital evidence can be a risky operation because data can be accidentally overwritten or lost while trying to retrieve it. Any alterations in data can change its meaning, or critical pieces of information, like the characters in a password, can be erased while mining data.

• The computer has to be left on while investigating it because a shut down can sometimes overwrite any evidence in temporary storage. Investigators have to disconnect the computer from its modem but leave both on in case the computer's owner could be monitoring the computer for intrusions.

• Investigators also need to be careful of business computers that are networked.

The science of computer forensics has expanded over the past few decades with the increase of electronic communication.

Disconnecting a computer from its network might add additional unwanted data to its memory. In advance of data collection, investigators will usually work with the company's system administrators to be sure they know how things are set up.

• If this is a clandestine search where a computer must be seized while a suspect is elsewhere, investigators have to sketch or photograph the entire computer and modem setup so they can get the information they need and reassemble everything exactly the way they found it.

- Like other forms of forensic evidence, if digital data is not handled appropriately or the legal grounds for obtaining it are not met, that evidence might not hold up in court. Proper evidence-collection procedures and a good chain of custody must be maintained every step of the way.

- The no. 1 rule for digital investigators is the same as it is for all of us who use computers: Make a backup. Since digital files can be destroyed, changed, or damaged by working with them, it is imperative that investigators work from a copy on a special-examination computer so that the original data stays intact.

- Investigators first make a working copy master, which they archive. Other copies are made from that first download, and it is those versions investigators actually work on, while the working copy master is safely stored. Investigators can make a fresh copy from the archived working copy master at any time without having to go back to the original device.

- The technology itself keeps the chain of custody for the working copy master and all versions made from it within the device they are using to analyze the digital evidence. Digital devices time-date stamp things automatically. To make sure the data in each copy generation is an exact duplicate of the original, computer analysts use a hash function.

Retrieving Hidden and "Erased" Data
- Some data can often be retrieved from computer storage even after a person thinks it has been deleted. A hard disc contains tracks, like a phonograph record, and is divided, like a pie, into units called sectors. Data itself gets written into clusters, which are series of contiguous tract sectors.

- When a disc is newly formatted, files tend to be written on contiguous clusters. But over time, the disc begins to fill up with files of all sizes. The computer will break large files up to put some of it in other available clusters, which may or may not be adjacent. When this happens, the hard drive disc is said to be fragmented.

- Any leftover space in a cluster is called slack space. When somebody tries to save a new file, the operating system will not use up the slack space in a half-full cluster; it will go to a new cluster. Computers use slack space for other sorts of internal tasks, such as temporary data storage.

- Thus, when we think data is deleted and gone, a copy may still be sitting there in slack space. Users cannot normally access slack space, but computer forensic experts have special software tools that let them access it.

- Computer forensics experts use some of the same search features that we use on our own computers, such as browsing and keyword searching, but savvy computer criminals will often use code words.

- Investigators can use metadata searches to find information about a file, like who created it, when it was created, who it was sent to, and when it was received to develop a timeline of the crime, which might show opportunity or negate a suspect's alibi. They can also use automatic log searches created by computer programs to record activity; these will show when someone was online, or when a file was moved from one place on the computer into another folder, and so on.

- It is not just property crimes that leave digital clues, so can violent acts like kidnapping and murder. The 2004 murder of Jennifer Corbin, by her husband Dr. Barton Corbin, was solved by tracing his cell phone records. Not only that, the similarities of that murder to the alleged suicide of Dolly Hearn (one of Corbin's girlfriends), 14 years earlier, led to his confession to Hearn's murder as well.

Suggested Reading

Carrier, *File System Forensic Analysis*.

Casey, *Digital Evidence and Computer Crime*.

Kranacher, Riley, and Wells, *Forensic Accounting and Fraud Examination*.

Nelson, Phillips, and Steuart, *Guide to Computer Forensics and Investigations*.

Peterson, *Understanding Surveillance Technologies*.

Questions to Consider

1. What is digital evidence?

2. How is digital evidence different from computer evidence?

3. What types of crimes might include digital evidence?

Structure Failure—Forensic Engineering
Lecture 15

Forensic engineering specialists are responsible for determining what went wrong in the event of major disasters that result in the collapse of man-made or natural structures. Engineers and builders have a legal responsibility to meet certain standards and plan for worst-case scenarios. When a storm or an earthquake takes out a bridge, or when a group like the September 11th terrorists cause a building collapse, forensic engineers can determine why the builders best-laid plans have failed.

The Purpose of Design Standards
- Good design is no accident, and ensuring that the things we need to work for us are functional and safe cannot be left to chance. A civil lawsuit prompted by negligent construction or poor manufacturing might carry huge financial penalties. It is difficult for a judge or jury to put a dollar amount on the loss of life, health, productivity, or state of mind, but decisions like that are made every day.

- We have standards that govern the production of the objects around us. As consumers and users of things made by others, we need to be able to trust that those who construct and produce the things in our environment do so carefully, ethically, and to the standards society has agreed on.

- When that trust is broken by negligence, carelessness, or maliciousness—or corners are cut to save money, giving consumers less than what they have coming to them—we have agreed as a society the manufacturers of those products are liable for the damage they cause.

- Unforeseen issues of planning, implementation, and use can arise. Even rigorous testing may not have uncovered a design flaw in a product or vehicle. And of course, accidents happen for all kinds of reasons, from weather-related incidents to malicious acts like sabotage and terrorism.

- The science of figuring out the cause of material, product, and structural failures is known as forensic engineering. Forensic engineers use the principles of physics, chemistry, biology, design, and construction, among other things, to analyze fault and mechanism when things go wrong.

Structural Integrity

- The collapse of the Tacoma Narrows Bridge, colloquially known as Galloping Gertie, in a wind storm in November 1940 is a classic case used in nearly every physics or forensic engineering book. Some theories attributed its failure to mechanical resonance—that is, the wind shook the bridge at a frequency matching the bridge material's natural frequency, called its resonance frequency. Other sources attribute the structural failure to aeroelastic flutter, in which winds caused fluttering waves of motion that ultimately tore the structure into pieces.

- Structural integrity refers to how soundly a structure is built for its purpose and, as a result, how well it holds up in the variety of conditions to which it might be subjected. The root causes of poor structural integrity usually boil down to 2 types of support inadequacies—static load deficiencies and dynamic load deficiencies.

- Static includes the basic weight of a structure; in other words, the structure has to be strong enough to withstand gravity and hold itself up. Static load is often broken down to 2 components, called dead load and live load.

- The dead load is the actual weight of the materials that make up the structure. The live load is the part of the weight that changes, including factors like people, furnishings, machinery, weather, and how that weight is distributed throughout the space.

- Dynamic load relates to forces that change over a short period of time. In the case of a bridge, for example, an increased dynamic load could result from a lot of trucks that are over the weight limit repeatedly traveling over it. Dynamic loads also include natural forces like earthquakes, tornados, tsunamis, and high winds.

- Like people, buildings, bridges, and other structures age. Over time, the ability of a structure to support its static and dynamic loads decreases because of factors like corrosion and weathering. Structures are therefore engineered to support static loads that are much heavier than the actual loads expected in regular use, and are regularly inspected over time.

- Designers and architects refer to this bonus engineering as the structure's margin of safety. A structure can collapse, even under normal use and expected dynamic loads, if the margin of safety was miscalculated.

- Some buildings have lasted many centuries or more, and some materials and design styles are just inherently better than others. Then again, acts of nature or other attacks can level even the most well-built structures.

When Engineers Cut Corners

- In January of 1919, in Boston, Massachusetts, in a warmer than normal winter, a 2.3-million-gallon molasses storage tank towering 50 feet in the air suffered complete structural failure and sent a flood of molasses barreling through the city streets at about 35 miles an hour. It almost sounds comical until you realize that 21 people were drowned or crushed to death, and over 150 were injured.

- The precise cause of the tank's failure will never be known. Some theorize that fermentation of the molasses—which could have been accelerated by the warm weather—caused carbon dioxide pressure to rapidly build within the tank, causing a fatigue crack in the base of the tank to propagate. There was little doubt in the minds of many that the true fault rested with the construction of the tank, during and after which there was apparently no safety testing.

- Because the quality of design and how structures function over time and temperature is something that may not be understood until accidents happen, construction methods and standards evolve. Numerous building and manufacturing codes have come into existence to protect the public and consumers from danger by setting minimum construction standards.

- In 1981, a dance party on the skywalks of the Hyatt Regency Hotel in Kansas City, Missouri, led to their collapse, killing 114 people and injuring 200 others. Investigators studied both the original building plans and the structure as built and discovered an unexpected design change: The contractor that made the rods that suspended the skywalks asked to change the one-piece rods to 2-piece rods to make them easier to manufacture and hang.

- This change in fabrication shifted the way the static and dynamic loads were carried by the skywalk. Investigators also determined that the raised walkways were designed for a modest amount of foot traffic, not a large number of people dancing. They estimated that the total load at the time of the collapse was more than double the weight architects had designed them to hold—notwithstanding the design flaw.

The World Trade Center Collapse

- In the United States, the National Bureau of Standards was developed in 1901 and became known as the National Institute of Standards and Technology in 1988. Its engineers, scientists, and other technology experts are charged with identifying and promoting appropriate measurements, calibration standards, and quality-control benchmarks for all kinds of manufacturing and construction.

- One of the bureau's subcommittees, the National Construction Safety Team Advisory Committee, was charged with the monumental task of analyzing the 2001 collapse of the World Trade Center's twin towers.

- When designers conceived the towers, they actually took airplane impacts into consideration, because in 1945 a U.S. Army B-25 bomber had hit the nearby Empire State Building. Their most probable worst-case scenario for the World Trade Center used a single Boeing 707, which was—at the time—the largest aircraft in the world. The designers also assumed an accidental impact during takeoff or landing at speeds around 180 miles an hour.

- On September 11, 2001, the towers were struck by 2 Boeing 767s, each weighing almost 30 tons more than the Boeing 707 and carrying 10,000 gallons more jet fuel and traveling at a cruising speed of 530 miles an hour—almost 3 times faster than the takeoff and landing speed of the worst-case projections.

- The initial horizontal impact on the North Tower severed about 2/3 of the steel supports on the tower's north side. Six floors were damaged directly but did not collapse at this point. The resulting fire burned for 102 minutes before the North Tower collapsed.

- A short time later, the next Boeing 767 flew into the South Tower. This time, 9 floors were damaged during the impact at a lower point on the building. The impact

© John Foxx/Stockbyte/Thinkstock.

A domino effect of collapsing floors is what ultimately brought down the World Trade Center's twin towers.

caused similar structural damage to the steel supports, and after only 56 minutes of burning, the South Tower came down.

- Structurally, those towers were technically able to withstand those impacts, even though the hits each took were much greater than the expected worst-case scenario. What doomed the towers to collapse was the fire. In the case of the South Tower, each floor was covered in about 9 ounces of jet fuel per square foot, with a potential to burn at 3140°F (although the actual fire temperature was several hundred degrees lower).

- The major effect of the fire on the structural integrity of the World Trade Center towers was on the steel supports and the concrete around that steel. Steel-reinforced concrete degrades and cracks at temperatures over 120°F. At 1000°F, the structural steel supports lose about half their tensile strength. At 1300°F, steel is no longer even viable in its support capabilities.

- When the structural components of steel and concrete failed on the 6 floors in the North Tower and the 9 floors in the South Tower, they could no longer carry their loads. The South Tower fell first, even though it was struck second, because there were 16 floors above the impact zone weighing down on the 9 damaged floors, compared to the North Tower, which had 11 floors bearing down on the 6 damaged floors.

- The undamaged part of each building came crashing down, as one unit, with all of its weight, onto the damaged area—a direct vertical dynamic load. Their mass was too much for the floors below to hold, and then each floor gave way in turn, causing the pancaking collapse we all witnessed, until the entire tower was gone.

- Figuring out what went wrong in any type of catastrophe like this is the responsibility of forensic engineering specialists. Even in natural disasters, like Hurricane Katrina, the expertise of forensic engineers is called on, for example, to try to determine whether or

Lecture 15: Structure Failure—Forensic Engineering

110

not faulty construction was to blame for the many levees that failed during the storm surge.

Suggested Reading

Carper, *Forensic Engineering*.

Delatte, *Beyond Failure*.

Noon, *Engineering Analysis of Fires and Explosions*.

———, *Forensic Engineering Investigation*.

———, *Introduction to Forensic Engineering*.

Ratay, *Forensic Structural Engineering Handbook*.

Why the Towers Fell.

Questions to Consider

1. What are some possible uses of engineering in forensic science?

2. What types of sciences and technologies are used in forensic engineering analyses?

3. Can you think of specific instances or cases—besides those in the lecture—in which forensic engineering has been used to explain a sequence of events?

Forensic Analysis of Vehicle Accidents
Lecture 16

A nalysis of motor-vehicle crashes relies, fundamentally, on Newton's laws of motion, but accurate accident reconstruction is far from simple. Forensic engineers use a wide variety of evidence, from skid marks and crash-test statistics to modern innovations like black-box data. This work is not only important in understanding individual accidents, it has led to the development of safer vehicles.

Vehicle Accident Statistics

- In 1900, only about 8000 cars were registered in the United States; by 1915, there were more than 2.3 million cars on the developing U.S. road system. Today, there are over 250 million registered passenger vehicles in the United States—over half are cars and the rest are SUVs, light trucks, and motorcycles.

- The number of accidents per capita in the United States varies depending on location, with city streets being safer than country roads in terms of fatal crashes when comparing population base to miles driven. At the same time, safety improvements have decreased fatalities from motor-vehicle accidents significantly; in the last 3 decades of the 20th century, the death rate from traffic injuries was cut by 50%.

- The decline in accident fatalities seems to relate to 3 main factors: a dramatic increase in seat belt and child car seat use; a major reduction in drunk driving; and the effort to design safer vehicles by car companies. Some of those changes were due to legislation, some to social activism and driver awareness, and some because of lawsuits among insurance companies or against car manufacturers.

- The most common causes of vehicular accidents, other than driving under the influence of alcohol or other drugs, include right-of-way mistakes, failure to yield, excessive speed, following too closely, disregarding traffic signals, and otherwise "imprudent" driving styles. Interestingly, equipment failure is not a significant cause of motor-vehicle accidents.

- Almost half of fatal accidents are collisions between vehicles; about a quarter are collisions with fixed objects like telephone poles, overpass and bridge supports, and trees. A little over 10% of fatalities involve pedestrians being struck, and just over 10% are considered noncollisions—things like going off a cliff. Accidents involving bikes, scooters, and the like cause about 2% of traffic fatalities, and those with trains are about 1%. Fatalities due to collisions with deer and other animals amount to only 0.2%.

Analyzing Accident Scenes

- Analysis of motor-vehicle accidents involves Newton's laws of motion, as well as the conservation of energy and conservation of momentum principles. But the data investigators use also comes from specific and more familiar things at the scene of an accident like the length of skid marks, the positions where vehicles come to rest after the accident, the direction they were traveling before the accident, and the point of impact, if they can be figured out.

- To gather this kind of data, the law enforcement officer who documents the accident scene has to create the equivalent of a crime-scene sketch of the area, complete with accurate measurements. He or she will also have to look at the damage to the vehicles and other objects involved.

- The investigator notes the location of crash debris, looks for impact and paint transfer evidence on both cars, and assesses the road-worthiness of the vehicles both before and after the accident. The investigating team will also have to note the road and weather conditions at the time of the accident and figure out the physical and mental conditions of the drivers.

- Time and speed are difficult to judge when you are in the moment of an accident. Each driver typically underrepresents his or her own speed and overrepresent the speed of any other vehicle involved. Different people can judge any event differently, depending on their perspective or involvement, like whether the light was green, yellow, or red when a car went through it.

- Forensic engineers who reconstruct accidents are seldom, if ever, at the scene just after it occurs. They may be crunching the data weeks after the accident, or maybe even years later, if they're offering a second opinion before a trial. They use the accident report from the investigating scene officers, photographs taken by police or insurance estimators, the vehicles—or what is left of them—and statements from the drivers or witnesses.

The Mathematics of a Crash
- Kinetic energy is the energy of motion. Work, in physics, is the force needed to overcome resistance and produce change. When a vehicle is moving, it has kinetic energy, which is determined relative to its speed and mass. Stopping—whether by coasting, breaking, or hitting something—means that the kinetic energy of that vehicle has to get to zero.

- The kinetic energy of a moving vehicle, is one half of the product of its mass and squared velocity ($\frac{1}{2}mv^2$). Since velocity is squared, when speed doubles, the kinetic energy increases by a factor of 4. So, if you are going 50 miles an hour, you will need 4 times the distance to brake as you would if you were going just 25 miles an hour. The damage to a vehicle and its occupants, or a pedestrian that it hits, also increases with speed.

- The speed at the time of the accident has to be estimated after the accident. The physics principle of conservation of energy sets forth that the total energy at the beginning of the physical processes involved in the accident is equal to the total energy at the end of the physical processes involved in the accident.

- The accident includes what investigators call "irreversible work" like braking, skidding, and crushing. They use up some of the energy in an accident and cannot be converted back into energy of motion. The rubbing of the brake pads on the brake disk or drum, for example, irreversibly changes some of the energy of the moving vehicle into friction and heat.

- If you are trying to bring a car to a complete stop, that heat loss and friction will continue until all of the energy of the moving car is used up and the vehicle comes to a halt. But in an accident, the energy of the car in motion can be irreversibly changed in other ways, like by producing a skid or crumpling the bumper.

- The investigator can measure the skid mark and figure out how fast the vehicle was traveling at the time the driver first slammed his foot on the brake. To get an accurate calculation, the type of road surface and how wet or dry it was need to be considered. There are specific standards, called frictional coefficients, for different types of tires and pavement.

In plastic collisions, the car parts that hit are damaged to the point where they can't snap back to their original condition.

- The damage to a vehicle's front end can also help determine how fast it was going at the time of a crash. Crash test data produced by government and private agencies establishes crush-versus-speed relationships for different types of vehicles, called energy-to-crush depth coefficients. The average crush depth across the damaged part of the car tells the investigator how much energy that car spent when it crashed into whatever it hit. Then that, in turn, shows how fast it was going at the time.

- The driver's body is being propelled at the same speed as the car; therefore, the driver hits the inside of the car at the same speed as the car hits another object. That is why car interiors have been redesigned over the years to include not only better safety restraints and airbags but also collapsible steering columns and engines that slide beneath the car rather than through it.

- Because more than half of all collisions happen between 2 cars—both of which are usually moving—the calculations get a little more complicated. When 2 cars run into each other they exert equal but opposite forces on each other, following Newton's third law of motion. These forces sum to zero unless some other external force is applied.

- Momentum is the velocity of an object times its mass, or $p = mv$. The law of conservation of momentum states that when 2 vehicles crash into each other, their momentum just before the crash is equal to their momentum just after they have hit.

- For example, if a car is sitting still at a stop sign and someone rear-ends it, the stopped car will move forward because the moving car will slow but some of the moving car's momentum will transfer to the stopped car. If either car leaves skid marks, investigators can use a combination of skid-mark measurement and momentum calculation to figure out how fast the moving driver was going when he hit the stopped car.

Beyond the Math

- Distracted drivers often leave clues for investigators like open maps, cell phones, headphones, open makeup containers, splattered food, or a loud stereo to incriminate themselves. Accident investigators also consider evidence about a person's sobriety at the time of a crash, which might come in the form of alcohol and drug paraphernalia.

- Sometimes drunk or high drivers try to put the blame on each other—even to the point of changing seats with a sober (or deceased) passenger. Investigators use all available clues to evaluate the position of occupants at the time of the accident, like bloodstain and injury patterns, especially in crashes where the sobriety of the driver might be at issue.

- The filaments in car light bulbs can show whether exterior lights were on or off at the time of an accident. That can be used to see if the headlamps or a turn signal was on at the time of the crash, which might corroborate or refute somebody's statement.

- These days, many cars have technology that has the capability to tell its own side of the story. Black-box technology, similar to that found in airplanes, can be found in some vehicles for capturing information in case of an accident.

Learning from Accidents

- In the crash of American Eagle Flight 4184 out of Indianapolis, Indiana, which happened on Halloween 1994, the data recorder captured far more than just speed; it registered a terrifying series of events in flight. The type of plane involved—the ATR 72—had already been implicated as prone to equipment failure, particularly during icy conditions, and that is apparently what happened in this case. As a result of that accident, and other incidents involving the same type of plane, ATR-72s, are only permitted to fly in warmer climates today.

- Another tragic equipment and temperature combination apparently caused the Space Shuttle Challenger disaster in 1986, killing all 7 of its crew, including the highly-publicized first "teacher in space"— Christa McAuliffe. It was ultimately determined that the morning's cold temperatures likely caused a failure of a simple piece called an O-ring that served as a seal in a solid rocket booster. This tragedy also pointed to some major disconnects between management and science within NASA that needed to be addressed.

- These types of tragedies—from car accidents to plane crashes to space travel disasters—all have the power to promote change. As sad as these accidents are, they do promote better and safer vehicles, as well as remind us all to be more careful when we drive.

Suggested Reading

Burke, *Forensic Medical Investigation of Motor Vehicle Incidents*.

Noon, *Forensic Engineering Investigation*.

———. *Introduction to Forensic Engineering*.

Ratay, *Forensic Structural Engineering Handbook*.

Questions to Consider

1. What do you know about the analysis of vehicular accidents?

2. How has the analysis of motor-vehicle accidents changed how and what we drive?

3. What are Newton's laws of motion, and how are they relevant to accident reconstruction?

Fire Science and Explosion Forensics
Lecture 17

Fires and explosions can occur naturally, so forensics experts look for specific clues to determine when arson and deliberate bombing have taken place. Investigators collect evidence about a fire or explosion's point of origin, the chemical composition of the materials involved, the spread of damaged objects and debris, even standard forensic evidence like fibers, fingerprints, and DNA to create a complete picture of an incident's cause.

Arson Facts and Statistics

- Fire happens when oxygen combines with some fuel in the presence of heat. The dancing flames we observe are gases burning as the combustion takes over one substance after another in its path.

- Some fires, and even some explosions, are truly accidents. But how do investigators determine this? Unlike in the courtroom where innocent until proven guilty is the rule, since any incident could be a crime scene, suspicious until proven otherwise is the way all cases of fire and explosion are approached.

- Investigators look for accelerants, igniters, bomb fragments, and explosive residues. They also look for the point of origin in a fire; multiple origins nearly always rule out an accident. Other evidence of a fire that was intentionally set could include signs of a breaking and entering.

- The most common motive for arson is to destroy evidence of some other crime—like murder, burglary, or embezzlement. Another common reason is insurance fraud. Intimidation, extortion, terrorism, or sabotage can also drive people to arson, as can emotions like revenge, jealousy, or hatred. Some arson is caused by vandalism, and it is estimated that half of all arson arrests involve juveniles.

- Occasionally, an arsonist will set a fire and then "discover" it to seem heroic. Research has shown that babysitters, volunteer librarians, night-watch personnel, and security guards are among the most common of these misguided heroes, as are some volunteer firefighters.

- According to FBI statistics, in 2010, about 45.5% of arson offenses involved a structure. Another 26% of arsons targeted vehicles. The other 28.5% of intentionally set fires began outdoors, in timber, grass, or crops.

- Arsons in industrial and manufacturing settings resulted in the highest average dollar loss, at about $133,700 per fire event. In 2008, it was estimated there were 14 times more arson fires in impoverished neighborhoods compared to wealthier areas.

The Basics of Explosives
- The chemistry and physics are somewhat different from fires. An explosive is a material capable of rapid conversion from a solid or liquid state to a gas. That conversion results in energy released as heat, pressure, and sound waves.

- All explosions, except nuclear ones, are similar to fire in many ways, but explosions give off more energy than fires for a given amount of fuel, and the oxygen is mixed into the fuel during an explosion, rather than coming from the surrounding air as during a fire.

- The damaging effects of fire include the heat that melts objects, the burning that can reduce materials to ash, and smoke damage (which also carry soot deposits and disperse chemicals from burned objects). Smoke inhalation kills far more people who die in fires than the flames themselves.

- Explosions have their own set of damage mechanisms: The escaping gases from the blast pressure, called a positive pressure blast, can travel thousands of miles an hour away from the explosion site and exert hundreds of tons of pressure per square inch.

- This blast creates a partial vacuum at the explosion site that, in turn, sucks air, gases, and debris from the explosion back toward the site of detonation during the negative pressure phase of a blast. It is not as strong as the initial positive pressure blast, but it can still do a lot of damage.

- Explosions also produce fragmentation not seen in fires. The casing on a bomb can shatter and produce shrapnel that can tear apart any objects or people it hits. As the blast fragments objects in its path, those fragments can become projectiles, too. Bombers can also put nails or other pieces of metal inside the bomb casing to create additional damage.

- Typically the least damaging consequences of an explosion are its thermal effects. Sometimes there's a fireball at the moment of detonation. When high explosives are used, the thermal effects are hot and quick; with low explosives, the thermal effects are cooler but longer in duration. An explosive fireball tends to burn out quickly, unless other materials catch fire.

Investigating Fires and Explosions
- When a fire is discovered or an explosion happens, the first responders have 2 main priorities: Get everyone trapped by the fire or blast to safety, then put out the fire and/or ensure there are no more explosions. Only after those 2 things are tended to will an investigation begin.

- Collecting evidence at the scene of a fire can be far more complicated than in most other forensic investigations. Lighting and temperature control were likely taken out by the incident, the structure under investigation may be unstable, investigators may be slogging around in piles of wet materials, and hazardous fumes and residues may be present.

- Victims can be nearly completely incinerated by fire, and the highly pressurized water coming out of fire hoses can cause additional damage. Objects can be nearly obliterated by fires and blasts, and even common household and personal items may be difficult to identify. Explosions can rip objects and people apart, or throw them a considerable distance away—all complicating the investigation.

- As with any crime scene, firefighters, rescue personnel, utility workers, police officers, and even onlookers can taint a fire or explosion scene before investigators even get there. This can damage existing evidence, and may even introduce irrelevant footprints, fingerprints, fibers, DNA, or other material. But the need to rescue people and secure the scene takes priority over evidence preservation.

- Investigators collect pieces of burnt or partially burned wood, carpeting, and other materials, as well as control samples from unburned or undamaged areas for comparison if available. Samples of flammable liquids that may have been used as accelerants are collected. (Gasoline is the accelerant of choice in more than 50% of all arson fires.)

- Carpet, bedding, upholstered furniture, clothes, soil, and other absorptive materials have the most potential to retain unburned accelerant for sampling and lab analysis. Forensic labs use the same tests to figure out the nature of an accelerant as they use for identifying other chemicals, such as gas chromatography and mass spectroscopy. Investigators have many tools to detect accelerants, like chemical analyzers called hydrocarbon sniffers, as well as arson dogs.

- One clue that a fire is arson is the presence of a branching pattern called a fire trail, which does not occur in an accidental structure fire. This happens when an arsonist pours an accelerant on the floor from room to room and then lights it on the way out.

- Investigators also look for the source of ignition for a fire or whatever served as the detonator in an explosion. An igniter can be as simple as a burned match, which could possibly be linked through microscopic examination to a matchbook in a suspect's possession. A matchbook, lighter, or candle left at an arson scene might have fingerprints on it, and if a cigarette was used to start a fire, there could be DNA on the cigarette butt.

- Analysts will also look for timing devices—anything that could be used to delay ignition of a fire or an explosion so that the perpetrator can get away before the destruction starts either for his or her own safety or to avoid suspicion. These timing devices can range from simple, like a pack of matches wrapped around a burning candle, to very complex, like the cell phone bomb detonators seen in movies.

Types of Explosives

- Low explosives include the black powder and smokeless powder we talked about in our firearms discussion; both of these are commonly used in pipe bombs, where a section of metal pipe is stuffed with a low explosive, and when the bomb is detonated, the pipe fragments or sharp objects inside the pipe become shrapnel.

- Another common low explosive is ammonium nitrate and fuel oil, or ANFO. This was used in the bombing of the Oklahoma City Alfred P. Murrah Federal Building in 1995, by Timothy McVeigh, Terry Nichols, and their accomplices. The ammonium nitrate from plant fertilizer provides the oxygen source; when soaked in fuel oil, the mixture becomes highly explosive.

- High explosives include things like nitroglycerin, dynamite (which is nitroglycerin mixed with diatomaceous earth and calcium carbonate) TNT (or tri-nitro-toluene), and the military explosive called C4. Some high explosives, including nitroglycerin, are quite sensitive to heat and shock and are only used in small quantities as a primary explosive to detonate a secondary explosion.

- Secondary high explosives are more stable, easier to transport, and need a booster charge to detonate. Dynamite, TNT, and C4 are examples of secondary high explosives. Plastique, that moldable explosive sometimes seen in movies, is an example of a booster.

Where Fire Science Meets Other Forensics

- Investigators look for what is left of explosive devices, which are often homemade, as well as delivery method. Was it in a backpack left on the floor of a building, did it come through the mail, did it come in a vehicle? Investigators also need to determine the skill level necessary to make the bomb to hone in on whether their suspect is an amateur or an expert.

- In a business, investigators collect partially destroyed papers for analysis. Questioned-document examiners and forensic accountants may be able to piece together the evidence, establish a pattern of destroyed or missing documents, and establish a motive.

- Where there are injuries and fatalities, arson and explosives investigators may have to work with emergency-room personnel or

Some fires are truly accidents, such as when an appliance malfunction causes a house fire, but others are not.

forensic pathologists to collect evidence in or on the victim's body. An autopsy will also help establish whether the fire or explosion was the actual cause of death or whether the victim was murdered and then the blaze or blast executed to cover up the killing.

- Recent research suggests that setting a fire to cover up a murder is much more common than formerly thought. It was once believed that a human head would explode during a fire because so often incinerated remains would show a badly fragmented skull. Now, many previous death investigations involving fire scenes have been called into question; badly fragmented skulls are much more indicative of blunt-force trauma from bludgeoning, or shattered skulls from gunshot wounds.

- Other typical evidence may be present at fires and explosions, like glass, fibers, hair, shoe prints, or blood. But this evidence is collected differently than it would be at a nonfire scene. Any evidence needs to be kept in sealed, airtight containers because many accelerants are volatile and could evaporate. Explosives are not volatile, so that evidence does not have to be packaged in the same way.

- In suicide bombings, there are often telltale signs of who was carrying the bomb among the human remains. The bomber clearly sustains the most body fragmentation from the blast, and many body parts cannot be recovered because they were literally blown to bits.

- If any natural fuels that would have normally been present at the scene could not have reached the projected temperatures on their own, that usually points to an accelerant. When investigators see a pile of wood or rags in a structure where they would not normally be located, that is a clue to the origin of an arson fire.

- Arsonists also typically start fires on the lower floors of a large building. If the point of origin is on the 14th floor of an office building, it is less likely to be arson since it would have taken much more time for the perpetrator to get out—and think of all the witnesses or surveillance cameras they might have to pass during their exit.

- If the point of origin seems to be a space heater, or a candle left burning on a dining room table, investigators may quickly have their answer and move on, but regardless of the circumstances, point of origin determination is standard in all fire investigations. This not only helps establish the cause, which can be important for insurance purposes, but can lead to safer appliances and lives saved.

Suggested Reading

Almirall and Furton, *Analysis and Interpretation of Fire Scene Evidence.*

"Arson."

Lentini, *Scientific Protocols for Fire Investigation.*

Marshall and Oxley, *Aspects of Explosives Detection.*

Noon, *Engineering Analysis of Fires and Explosions.*

———, *Forensic Engineering Investigation.*

Stauffer, Dolan, and Newman, *Fire Debris Analysis.*

Questions to Consider

1. What are the 2 major differences between a fire and an explosion?

2. How are the damaging effects of fires different from those of explosions?

3. What are the roles and responsibilities of an arson investigator at a crime scene?

Blood Evidence—Stains and Spatters
Lecture 18

B loodstain analysis is a complex and occasionally controversial part of forensic investigation. Investigators use the known physical qualities of blood and surfaces, the biological behavior of blood as it leaves the body, and the physics of weaponry to reconstruct crimes from blood evidence left at a scene. This evidence can be used to determine things like the relative locations and sizes of the perpetrator and victim and sometimes even hint at the perpetrator's state of mind.

Bloodstain Analysis Enters the Mainstream

- Analyzing bloodstain patterns goes back well into human prehistory, when our ancient ancestors tracked wounded animals in much the same way that a hunter would today. Using bloodstain interpretation in modern forensic investigations first appears in the 19th century in Europe.

- After a high-profile 1954 murder, bloodstain evidence was used in the controversial Dr. Sam Shepard case. Sheppard was accused of beating his wife to death, but a month after Sheppard's verdict, forensic scientist Dr. Paul Kirk visited the crime scene and used bloodstain patterns to help show the position of the victim and assailant, alleging that Mrs. Sheppard was beaten to death by someone left-handed. Dr. Sheppard was right-handed.

- Sheppard won a retrial in 1966 and was found not guilty in the second trial. Although this outcome was controversial, the Sheppard case was a major step in getting the legal system to accept bloodstain pattern evidence.

- The theoretical and scientific underpinnings of bloodstain pattern analysis have been argued by some to be highly variable and somewhat subjective, but that could be said for plenty of areas in forensic science.

The Basics of Blood

- Looking at a visible record of bloodshed in terms of the shapes, locations, and distribution patterns can give clues about the objects and forces that have generated the bloodstains. Examples include areas where blood has been ejected, sprayed, dripped, walked through, or smeared by the victim or perpetrator.

- This is an area of forensics where extensive photo documentation is crucial because it may be the only way to capture the evidence. For proper interpretation, bloodstain experts have to understand physics, the nature of blood and the cardiovascular system that moves it around, as well as the pathology of wounds. Clues can lead to the positions of the victim and perpetrator during an assault, as well as how many blows or shots were delivered and in what order.

- Depending on body size, the average adult has roughly 5 liters of blood, around 8% of total body weight. Blood plasma is the liquid fraction and is mostly made of water, along with some various ions, proteins, nutrients, and wastes. Red blood cells, white blood cells, and platelets—which are cell fragments—are suspended in the liquid blood plasma.

- When blood vessels are damaged, the lining of the vessel walls exposes proteins that attract blood platelets. The platelets then change their nature and stick to each other, forming a plug that can help close up a small wound. The damaged vessel walls and platelets also release chemicals that ultimately form a polymer of insoluble protein strands, called fibrin, that causes coagulation as the liquid plasma evaporates.

- Inside the body, blood movement is governed by the work of the heart acting as a pump, combined with the pressures within blood vessels. Other forces act on blood when it is outside the body, and this movement will depend, to some degree, on whether the heart is still beating or has stopped.

- Blood plasma, like other liquids, has cohesive properties that holds its molecules together and makes them flow; it also has surface tension. Outside the body, blood can separate into smaller droplets when gravitational or impact forces break its surface tension and viscosity. A drop of blood will form a sphere that minimizes its surface area. Once a drop forms, it will not fraction into smaller droplets unless it hits something or is acted on by another force.

Types of Bloodstains by Appearance

- The major types of bloodstains can be categorized based on their appearance. Some experts break bloodstains into 3 main groups: passive, spatter, and altered. Other experts prefer to focus on the speed of traveling blood and classify stains as low velocity, medium velocity, and high velocity.

- A major factor in how a stain will look is the type of surface that it hits. Blood will look and behave differently when it's on a smoothly painted wall, an upholstered piece of furniture, a leather car seat, rough concrete, carpeting, grass, and so forth.

- Passive bloodstains are the result of gravity, like when blood drips vertically, a pool of blood surrounds a bleeding victim, or large droplets of blood run down a surface. Some types of transfer stains are also considered passive, like when hands or fingers move blood from one surface to another, which is sometimes referred to as a swipe.

- Spatter stains result from the application of some other force besides gravity that affects the movement of blood. Here, investigators will see features that show directionality and distribution. This would include impact spatter from blunt-force trauma or gunshot wounds.

- Altered stains have been changed in some way, whether through natural clotting action, insect activity, or mixture with some other material, like soil. Altered stains also include blood evidence that has been modified when someone attempted to clean up a crime scene, which is called a wipe, rather than a swipe. Other stain alterations, called voids, represent an area where an object blocked the spatter of blood but was then picked up. Alteration can complicate bloodstain interpretation.

- Any circular distortion of a stain helps reveal the angle of impact on a flat surface. If there is a right angle between the blood source and the surface, there will be a nearly perfectly circular stain. The stain gets more elongated as the angle of impact decreases. So, if blood flew toward the surface at a low angle, the resulting stain will be very oblong.

- The oblong shape tells investigators about the direction the blood was traveling in, too. The more pointed end of the elongated droplet faces the direction of travel. The linear tip of the oblong stain may even be fractured because tiny blobs of blood break off from the surface of the parent stain once it hits, and they continue to travel even further.

- Surface texture is also a factor here. The harder and less porous the surface, the fewer tiny spatter droplets will result. Rough, textured surfaces show spines extending from their spatter droplets and can also show peripheral spatter that will complicate figuring out directionality.

- Investigators can figure the point of origin of a bloodstain if they have a group of related stains in a spatter pattern. Once they figure out the direction the spatter came from, they can take a half dozen or so really diagnostic elongated droplets and trace them to a point where their centerlines converge.

- From that horizontal point of origin on the flat plane where the spatter is, they use trigonometry to estimate the height above the surface where the blood drops were flying from. Sometimes on television you see this done with strings, and they call it "stringing the crime scene." These days, lasers and computerized software can do the necessary calculations.

Types of Bloodstains by Speed

- A low-velocity bloodstain pattern would be produced if a bleeding victim is still standing or walking away from an attack and some blood drips to the floor. These patterns are said to produce the greatest variety of shapes and sizes compared to medium- or high-velocity stains and are usually larger in size.

- Low-velocity drip patterns can produce some tiny droplets that fly off the edges of the drop of blood on impact. Blood experts call these satellite droplets, and they are more likely when drips of blood fall from a height or if someone steps in a pool of blood and splashes it.

- Medium-velocity spatter occurs when the moving blood is subjected to a force in addition to gravity—for instance, in cases of bludgeoning. Medium is typically defined as greater than 5 feet per second up to

For proper interpretation, blood-spatter experts have to understand physics, the nature of blood, and the pathology of wounds.

about 100 feet a second. When blood hits a surface at that rate, it will be broken up into smaller droplets, producing that fine pattern known as spatter.

- High-velocity patterns are usually said to result from blood traveling at speeds of greater than about 100 feet a second; this usually only occurs in gunshot wounds or where high-speed machines are involved. High-velocity bloodstains form tiny spatter patterns that are mistlike.

How Blood Leaves the Body

- When an artery is cut, blood will exit the body under greater pressure than when it flows from a vein. This is because blood pressure is much higher in arteries, and there are characteristic bloodstain patterns associated with arterial spurts. When a major artery like the carotid or femoral is cut, the rise and fall in blood pressure with the heart rate will cause an intermittent, arching, low-velocity pattern.

- When someone is forcefully coughing up blood after an injury to the face or chest—essentially choking on their own blood—the bloodstains will show a low-velocity spatter pattern, and sometimes investigators will see air bubbles in the droplets.

- How fresh a drop of blood is—especially as it is drying on a nonabsorbent surface—can sometimes be roughly approximated from skeletonization—the way the edges of a drop dry faster than the center.

- Castoff patterns are created by blood droplets being slung off of a moving bloody object, like a blunt-force weapon. The pattern is made in the opposite direction of the blows, when the perpetrator is making a backswing to strike again. The second and subsequent blows make the pattern, so when a cast-off pattern is clear, it can give investigators an idea of the minimum number of blows that were struck.

- The clothing of the killer can be analyzed for bloodstain patterns. This could include wipes, swipes, castoff, and sometimes back spatter from a gun. Sometimes the image of the weapon can even be transferred to clothing as if it were stamped in blood. A perpetrator can leave bloody footprints and fingerprints behind at a crime scene, too.

Fake Blood for Fun

You might want to make some of your own practice blood to repeat some of the experiments in this lecture yourself. I have tried quite a few fake blood recipes with my students, and some are better than others.

This recipe will not clot, but this is my preferred concoction because it has similar properties to fresh blood but it does not use anything too sticky or hard to clean up—although it will stain because it is made with (optional) food coloring.

- 500 ml powdered milk

- 325 ml water

- 1.5 oz. red food coloring

- 25 drops green food coloring

- 5 drops of blue food coloring

Slowly add the water to the powdered milk while stirring constantly until you get the right consistency, adjusting the water–to–powdered milk ratio as necessary. The mixture will keep for about a week or so, but the consistency might change over time.

Suggested Reading

Bevel and Gardner, *Bloodstain Pattern Analysis with an Introduction to Crime Scene Reconstruction.*

Englert, Passero, and Rule, *Blood Secrets.*

James, Kish, and Sutton, *Principles of Bloodstain Pattern Analysis.*

1. What kinds of information can be gained from examining the pattern of bloodstains at a crime scene?

2. Does the specific shape of a drop of blood have any meaning?

3. How do investigators document and collect patterns of blood spatter at a crime scene?

The Science of Death
Lecture 19

Before we can look at the forensics of death, it is important to have a scientific understanding of what death is. The definition is not as black and white as one might think. Death might be due to a chronic condition or an acute trauma; it might be a slow process or a sudden event, and various medical and legal standards have been developed to draw lines between living and dead.

Our Distance from Death

- You now know that "forensics investigation" is not synonymous with "death investigation," but certainly most people consider the most serious crimes to be those that result in the loss of life. Because of this, it is important to talk about the science of death—how death actually occurs and how it is defined, both medically and legally.

- Most people in the developed, modern world are removed or insulated from death and dying. In general, we no longer slaughter our own food; most of our deaths take place in hospitals and nursing homes. But death touches all of us, and learning about death can help prepare us for when it enters our lives.

- People talk about the moment of death, but the reality is a lot more complex. Few types of death take place in a single moment. Most last at least seconds, if not minutes, hours, or in some cases years.

- Death is a process, and our ability to define or determine when someone is actually dead is not always easy. It depends on our ability to accurately assess all body functions, which is not always as easy as you might think, even with modern medical equipment. As recently as the mid-1990s, there have been reported cases of "dead" people waking up in the morgue.

Cellular Death

- We are alive because our cells are alive and functioning, and we die when a significant number of the more important cells in our bodies die. Anyone who has survived a heart attack is living with some dead tissue in their heart. Stroke survivors carry around groups of dead brain cells. The amount of disability a person suffers after a major body trauma like that depends on what part of the heart or brain is damaged.

- Cells carry out all of the processes we associate with life, like metabolism, respiration, movement, and homeostasis—that is maintaining conditions such as temperature and blood pressure in response to external changes and stresses.

- Cells make up tissues, tissues make up organs, organs make up body systems, and those body systems are dependent on each other. A major failure in any one body system can put enough stress on an organism to cause its death.

Legal Death

- Modern science allows us to gauge the workings of body parts, including heart and brain function, with reasonable accuracy, but society still debates the definition of death. Modern technology also allows us to maintain certain body functions in people that can no longer perform them on their own, making it even more difficult to really say whether someone is dead or alive.

- Definitions of death have changed over time. In 1968, Harvard Medical School outlined the 4 features necessary to declare a person brain-dead: (1) The person must be both unreceptive and unresponsive; (2) They must have no breathing or movement; (3) They demonstrate no reflex activity; and (4) Their brainwave activity must show a flat line on an electroencephalogram, or EEG. The Harvard guidelines also recommended that the person be re-examined 24 hours later and show no change before they could be considered brain dead.

- In 1981, a U.S. presidential commission amended the Harvard standards to say that a skilled physician should be able to use a bedside exam along with their own judgment to establish that death has occurred, rather than rely on a battery of formal tests. This Uniform Determination of Death Act has been adopted in all 50 states. Among other reasons, this improves the chances of organs being viable for donation.

Causes of Death

- There are countless ways a person can die, some natural and some that attract the interest of forensic investigators. In the United States, ischemic heart disease—lack of sufficient blood flow to the heart, usually due to blocked arteries—is still the top killer, taking the lives of about 164 people in every 100,000 in the year 2000. By comparison, motor-vehicle accidents and suicide numbered 15 and 12 deaths per 100,000. Natural deaths of all kinds far outnumber the accidental.

- In terms of ischemic heart disease, Australia had a death rate in 2000 fairly comparable to the United States, Germany's was a little lower, and Canada's lower still. Ischemic heart disease deaths in Japan were far fewer—36 per 100,000. England and Wales had higher rates—198 per 100,000, and in Russia the number was 409 per 100,000.

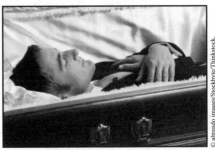

As creepy as it is, there have been cases in history where people have been accidentally buried alive.

- Despite the number of ways people can die, they can be boiled down to just one thing: People die because of an inability of the cardiovascular system to deliver oxygen and nutrients to cells. In chronic conditions, like heart disease, this is a gradual process. In acute causes of death, like a motor-vehicle accident, it happens quickly.

- Both chronic and acute deaths can be cause for a forensic investigation, because whenever there is an unexpected death, an autopsy may be needed. The key word is "unexpected." People who are expected to die are generally under a doctor's care, and as their chronic condition advances, more and more of their body cells malfunction or die, leading to tissues and organs with impaired functions. As organs fail one by one, body systems finally just shut down.

- Some chronic conditions do not directly end a person's life but are contributing factors. People with these diseases become less active and more disabled, and as fluid builds up in their lungs, bacterial growth can lead to pneumonia. The direct cause of death is the respiratory infection, but infection would not have happened if not for the underlying disease.

- In cases where a person has already been diagnosed with a serious disease, there is usually a typical and reasonably expected sequence of events that culminates in death. Unexpected deaths might also have an obvious cause, like an auto accident or gunshot. When a cause of death is both unexpected and obscure—say, a young athlete dies for no apparent reason during a football game—the cause might be easily explained during an autopsy.

Signs of Death
- Hospice is the international organization that specializes in care for people who are dying. One of their contributions to our understanding of the science of death has been to outline the physical changes that are to be expected when a person is approaching the end of life.

- When a person's body is shutting down from a chronic condition, they eat and drink less, sleep more, and have general body weakness. As the nutrient supply to the brain declines, they may show anxiety, confusion, and restlessness. A lack of fluid brings on dehydration.

- Because blood is mostly water, blood volume declines and so does blood pressure. The heart might try to compensate with a rapid but shallow heartbeat. Lowered blood volume alters blood chemistry, the driving force behind the movement of fluids into and out of body cells, so a person who is dying might have swelling in her arms and legs and that complicates blood flow even more.

- This so-called pre-active phase of death lasts around 2 weeks on average. Next, people move into the active stage of death, which usually lasts a few days, although in trauma cases, especially those involving massive bleeding, the active stage of death goes a lot faster, though some of the body changes are the same.

- During active death, the person may enter a coma or near coma state, becoming unresponsive to the outside world. Other people go to a different extreme, hallucinating or becoming very agitated. Breathing and heart rate grow increasingly abnormal; the respiration rate for someone who is actively dying ranges from 6 to 50 breaths a minute, whereas normal respiration rate is about 12 breaths a minute.

- Television and movies usually portray misleading death scenes— what we might call a pretty death. Death is seldom pretty. When people are dying, their mouths hang open. As they dehydrate, mucus collects in the throat, and breathing may become more of a gurgle or rasp. Blood leaves the skin and goes to deeper vital organs, so the skin looks blotchy and limbs may be cold to the touch.

- Because voluntary muscles relax in death, if a person's bowel or bladder is full, the contents may leak out at the time of death. The same loss of control over voluntary muscles will cause the jaw to go slack and eyelids to remain half open. Other body parts relax and respond to the pull of gravity, and death can look pretty peaceful especially compared to the struggle for breath that can be seen in an actively dying person.

- A common myth is that hair and fingernails continue to grow after death. In fact, the soft tissues of the scalp and the nail beds can dehydrate and pull back a bit away from the hair and nails, so it might look as if they have grown a little.

On the Scene of a Death

- The general guidelines for emergency personnel are that paramedics can withhold care when they encounter somebody whose trauma is so serious that their injuries are completely incompatible with life, like a victim who has been decapitated or is showing signs of rigor mortis.

- Laws vary from state to state in the United States, and decisions like these are often made between the on-scene emergency medical personnel and consulting physicians they are speaking to by radio or telephone.

- Paramedics and emergency medical people are often on the front lines of a number of situations that intersect with the forensic community. It is essential that any lifesaving measures be implemented before criminal activity is investigated, even though emergency workers can complicate a crime scene or a death investigation.

- Whatever is done, or not done, must be carefully documented so that all the pertinent information gets transferred to the coroner's or medical examiner's office not only from the crime scene but from the paramedics and the hospital, too.

- Forensic specialists known as death investigators or coroner's investigators are called to the scene in all cases of unexpected death. They relay pertinent information to the coroner or medical examiner so that appropriate decisions can be made.

- In most death investigations—at least in larger cities in the United States—the medical examiner or coroner does not visit the scene but relies on a death investigator to take photos and collect other information necessary to begin a forensic death investigation.

Suggested Reading

Iserson, *Death to Dust*.

Largo, *Final Exits*.

Murray, *Death*.

Nuland, *How We Die*.

Snyder Sachs, *Corpse*.

Questions to Consider

1. Is there truly a moment of death?

2. How does modern science determine that a person is dead?

3. What are some of the signs that death is imminent?

4. Do hair and nails continue to grow after death?

5. Do emergency medical personnel have the same responsibilities when dealing with a victim who is deceased versus alive?

Death Investigation—Algor, Livor, and Rigor
Lecture 20

Death investigators have the responsibility of beginning any inquiry into a questionable death. Acting as the medical examination team's eyes and ears at the scene, they gather all kinds of data that help establish cause and manner of death. These sometimes include obvious physical evidence, like a gunshot wound, but they also include documenting subtle—and some not-so-subtle—physical changes that take place after death.

Why Investigate a Death?

- Death investigators work side-by-side with law enforcement personnel, but with different objectives. Police must immediately concern themselves with the whodunit, but the death investigator tries to remain detached from that aspect—particularly if the death might have come at the hands of law enforcement or was a death in custody.

- In a sense, the death investigator needs to serve as the objective eyes and ears of the pathologist who may eventually conduct an autopsy. In consultation with the pathologist on duty, the death investigator will help determine whether or not the coroner or medical examiner should come to the scene.

- Through photographs and other documentation death investigators need to carefully convey the surroundings of the body back to the morgue, in addition to determining how and when to transport the body.

- Although laws vary in different states and countries, there are usually standard processes for reporting any death to public officials. Some deaths are straightforward and do not require a formal investigation. Other deaths might be considered questionable, or outright suspicious, and need a careful examination.

- Unlike the notion of innocent until proven guilty in the legal system, the rule of thumb in a death investigation is to assume foul play until shown otherwise. Deaths from negligence or carelessness may also result in a civil lawsuit. Manner of death may also affect life insurance payments or public health and safety.

- Some families also opt for nonforensic death investigations, often referred to as hospital autopsies, to find out something like whether their loved one died from an illness with a genetic component. Both forensic and nonforensic death investigations contribute to scientific research.

- In the United States, there are no federal laws that govern death investigation, but the Model Postmortem Examination Act, passed in 1954, helps states generate their own statutes. In general, a report must be made to a medical examiner for

  o Any circumstance where a death was definitely or possibly caused by violence.

  o Any death that may have been caused by a work-related or public health hazard.

  o Any death that happened in a public institution other than in a hospital setting.

  o And any sudden or unexpected death.

What a Death Investigator Does
- A death investigator has to collect as much information as possible about what happened around the time before and after the death occurred. Was any emergency medical aid given to the victim? Was the body moved or altered in any way? They also need to know things about the deceased's medical history, perhaps their social or personal history, and what the person was doing up to the time of death.

- The death investigator has to rely on witnesses or people who knew the deceased to get this information. This can involve asking some pretty sensitive questions, like whether the victim was depressed, did the person regularly see a doctor and why, what did the deceased last eat or drink, was the person known to take illegal drugs or engage in any risky or destructive behaviors, and so forth.

- The death investigator's role is not to solve any crime that might have occurred. It is to capture information that might be important to figuring out how or why a person died. This information is the link between the scene and the autopsy table. Usually, the death investigator examines only the body's surface and anything on it or in it. If authorities decide that a full or even a partial autopsy is needed, that will happen later at the morgue.

- A death investigator needs to document the condition of the body and where it was found, as well as who found it and when. Details like the victim's clothing, and whether it was in its normal place or condition might be important. Stains or tears on clothes

Death investigators are sent to the scene of a suspicious or unexpected death in the initial stages of inquiry.

© iStockphoto/Thinkstock.

or bed linens need to be noted. Any valuables or jewelry found on or with the body need to be carefully documented not only for safekeeping but also because they might play a role in identifying an unknown body.

- The investigator documents the temperature, humidity, air movement, and other specifics of the area where the body was found: Was the ground frozen, was the parking lot asphalt or concrete, what was the current like in the water. ... If there's a pool of blood around the body, its amount, color, and consistency need to be recorded.

- The death investigator also helps decide how to preserve evidence in or on the body—like bagging hands in case the perpetrator's tissue might be under the victim's nails, or using a clean, white sheet and a secure body bag to preserve any trace evidence. The investigator also has to document all visible injuries at the scene, since it is possible the body could be further damaged during transport.

Determining Time of Death

- When death occurs, all normal body metabolism stops, and the biochemical changes of decomposition start. Tissue decay can be broken down into 2 main overlapping causes: the chemical breakdown of cells and tissues and the action of bacteria living in and on the body.

- Regular body functions, like sweating, shedding our surface layer of skin cells, defecation, and urination, all contribute to unloading a certain number of our normal bacterial flora every day, and our immune functions help defend us from excessive parasite loads. But once a person dies, all of those normal functions stop, and the body becomes a reservoir of energy and nutrients for bacteria.

- How much decomposition occurs in the body, or even if it happens at all, mainly relates to the surrounding temperature. Cold temperatures help retard bacterial growth and prevent the chemical changes that happen in decaying organic matter, whereas warm temperatures can speed the process.

The 3 Mortises

- There are 3 types of mortis that set in after death: rigor mortis, livor mortis, and algor mortis. Livor mortis, sometimes just called lividity, is the settling of blood that starts to become visible as purplish discoloration on the skin's surface about an hour after death, due to the pull of gravity. Any pressure points on the body can show a different lividity pattern from the skin around them; for example, a tight waistband on pants might leave a paler area of skin.

- Within about 4 hours of death, livor is usually well-developed but might blanch out if finger pressure is applied. By around 8 hours of death, the patterns of blood pooling are usually fixed and will not change even if the body is moved.

- The discoloration of livor mortis remains until more advanced decomposition changes the normal skin tone in a process called marbling. Investigators look for other color changes in skin, too, like the cherry red color that might suggest carbon monoxide poisoning or a pink tone that might come from a cyanide death.

- Algor mortis is the change in body temperature that happens after death. Homeostatic mechanisms keep our body temperature at roughly 98.6°F or 37°C, with some minor fluctuations related to health and activity level. At death, the body starts to cool down. Algor mortis is therefore an important early indicator of the time since death.

- A death investigator needs to take the ambient temperature for potential comparison to the victim's body temperature. To get the core body temperature, some death investigators will use a thermometer probe that is inserted through the victim's skin into the liver.

- In a climate-controlled environment, body temperature remains fairly constant during the first hour after death. After the first hour, the body will lose heat at a rate of about 1.5°F, or about 0.83°C per hour. Determining time of death is a little trickier when a body is outdoors, where temperature varied more, and the usefulness of this measurement ends as soon as body temperature equals the ambient temperature. Over time, body temperature can even rise again as bacterial and insect activity start to generate heat.

- The condition of the body and how the person died can affect the ability of a death investigator to assess either livor or algor mortis. In such cases, they would use other factors to figure out time of death, like surveillance tapes or 911 call times. It is also important to check for algor and livor mortis even if a death was witnessed to corroborate the witness's story.

- Rigor mortis relates to the breakdown of organ systems, organs, and tissues after death. More specifically, it happens at the cellular level, part of the more widespread destruction of cells called autolysis.

- As normal cell functions break down and the energy needed for important cell processes like membrane function can no longer be produced, cell membranes disintegrate, and organelles that hold digestive enzymes begin to rupture. Other cell contents and molecules are destroyed.

- Spontaneous reactions occur as old chemical bonds break, and new bonds form within decaying tissue. Some of these reactions create new molecules, including cadaverine and putrescine. These are responsible for the odor that we associate with decomposing tissue.

- The activity of our muscles requires a constant source of the energy chemical called adenosine triphosphate, or ATP. When cell organelles no longer provide ATP, muscle cell proteins get stuck in a contracted phase.

- Rigor mortis does not last indefinitely. It usually sets in within a few hours and is fully established by about 12 hours, but as body tissues continue to disintegrate, within about 24 to 36 hours rigor mortis will end, and muscles become more gelatinous. So, rigor mortis is something else a death investigator might use to hone in on the time since death.

Other Bodily Changes
- Depending on how the body is dressed and whether it is indoors or outdoors, other changes might take place. Outdoors, the odor

147

of decomposition attracts insects and animals. Particularly in dry settings, the tips of the fingers and toes and the edges of the ears and lips can start to dry out and become leathery, which can distort facial features and make a person hard to identify.

- As the numbers of these bacteria grow in the gut of a person who has died, the body may bloat from the gases, especially in the abdomen. The only upside of this bloating is when it brings a drowning victim or a body that has been dumped in the water to the surface where it can be discovered and recovered. A major downside of this is that a decomposing body can literally burst from the pressures of these gases.

Suggested Reading

Bass and Jefferson, *Death's Acre*.

Hanzlick, *Death Investigation*.

Ribowsky, *Dead Center*.

Questions to Consider

1. How are the roles of a death investigator different from those of a crime-scene investigator?

2. What types of evidence does a death investigator collect?

3. Does a coroner or medical examiner always go to the scene where a questionable death has occurred?

4. What are some of the initial changes in the body when decomposition begins?

Autopsy—Cause and Manner of Death
Lecture 21

The main goal of an autopsy is to figure out why—the cause—and how—the manner—of a person's death. Not all deaths require an autopsy; however, when a coroner or medical examiner determines that an autopsy is needed, the work is carried out by a pathologist. Pathologists need a thorough knowledge of gross anatomy, cell biology, countless lab procedures, and even evidence-collection procedures to carry out their work.

Coroners and Medical Examiners

- The cause of death relates to what failure or trauma terminated a life, and there are so many ways this can happen we cannot discuss all of them in this course. Manner of death, on the other hand, is limited to only 5 possibilities, at least in most jurisdictions in the United States: natural death, accidental death, homicide, suicide, or unknown. Some jurisdictions add therapeutic complications to cover unexpected deaths that occur following medical procedures.

- Legally, both the cause and manner could be listed as unknown. When a skeleton is found in an abandoned building with no apparent trauma, there may be no way to know how or why that person died. Whatever the case, these determinations are left to the coroner or medical examiner in the jurisdiction where the remains were discovered.

- A coroner and a medical examiner are not the same thing. Generally, a coroner is an elected county official who may or may not be a medical doctor, depending on the law. Only 4 states in the United States—Ohio, Kansas, Louisiana, and North Dakota—require their county coroners to be doctors.

- In the majority of counties throughout the United States, there may only be a couple of deaths a year that need a formal investigation. It would be inefficient and cost prohibitive to hire a physician trained in medicolegal death investigations for that small of a caseload. Being coroner is thus usually a part-time job with a meager salary that is filled by a local election.

- Nonphysician coroners do not perform autopsies. Their job is to certify deaths in their jurisdiction and figure out when an autopsy is needed. Larger counties have the people and facilities to conduct their own autopsies; the smaller offices contract with larger agencies to do their autopsies.

- Under the alternate medical examiner or medical investigator system, the medical examiners are appointed by their state or county, rather than elected. In some states the medical examiner has to be a physician or even a forensic pathologist; in others, the title of medical examiner can be given to anybody responsible for death investigation, regardless of their education or employment background.

Who Performs an Autopsy?
- The Greek word "*autopsia*" means "to see with your own eyes." What someone is doing while conducting an autopsy, essentially, is using their own senses and knowledge to speak for a person who can no longer speak for themselves.

- Autopsies are done by medical doctors called pathologists who have special training in interpreting the physical signs of disease processes in the body. Pathology literally means "the study of suffering," but not all pathologists are forensic pathologists and not all even conduct autopsies.

- In the United States, forensic pathologists are medical doctors or osteopathic physicians who have specialized training beyond medical school. They have to understand the normal and abnormal structure and function of all tissues and organs, what happens to the body during all types of trauma, and the characteristic age-related changes in all parts of the body. They must be able to separate evidence of disease or injury present in the body prior to death from what actually caused the death.

Starting the Autopsy

- When a body comes into the morgue, the victim is logged in and their personal effects are documented and stored for safekeeping. The remains are weighed and measured. Based on information from the death investigator, the pathologist on duty—in consultation with the coroner or medical examiner—will decide whether the autopsy should be done immediately. If not, the deceased is added to the waiting list and the body is stored in a cooler.

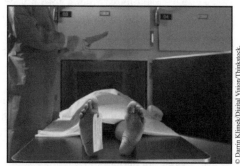

- For a standard forensic autopsy to be possible, the body must be fairly intact—that is, in the early stages **An autopsy forever changes a body, so it's important to document the appearance of the body as it is first observed.**
of decomposition. In such cases, a forensic pathologist will do a complete external exam, documenting the appearance of the body as they first observe it with both notes and photographs. They also look carefully for any trace evidence—like gunshot residue and fibers—on the surface of the body or clothing and collect it for the forensic science lab.

- Whole body X-rays might be taken either before or after the external exam. X-rays might show not only whether bones are broken but also foreign objects, like bullets, or some previous surgical procedures, like an artificial joint or surgical staples; these factors might give clues about a person's known health or could aid in identification.

- Next, clothing is removed to see body regions that were not visible during the initial exam. This is also when examinations and tests for sexual assault are performed, if necessary. After the pathologist feels sure that all surface trace evidence has been collected, the body might be washed. If any blood, gunpowder, dirt, or other material is cleaned away, they do a second external exam and might take more pictures. If surface trauma is found, detailed photos and descriptions are made.

- The pathologist might not only be looking for information about cause and manner of death, but if the body comes into the morgue as an unknown person, the autopsy needs to document anything that might be useful in figuring out the person's identity, like tattoos, scars, and other features.

- Fingerprints might be taken for a number of reasons. They could be used to identify an unknown person. They might be taken if the deceased is a suspect in a crime. Or they may be needed to compare with prints at the crime scene, to differentiate the victim's prints from the perpetrator's.

The Internal Autopsy
- The next step in a forensic autopsy is the internal examination, which is really a form of exploratory surgery. The pathologist begins with a Y-incision through the skin that runs from each clavicle toward the sternum, then down the chest and abdominal wall to the pubic bone. Once the skin is pulled back, an autopsy saw or rib cutter is used to open the chest, and a scalpel is used to open the abdominopelvic cavity.

- The pathologist will first make visual observations of the organs in place (call the in situ exam). Then they remove individual organs for a more detailed look. The size, color, density, and other features can say a lot about whether an organ is normal or not.

- A pathologist has to sort out pre-existing conditions from more proximal diseases or traumas that directly led to death, as well as overlapping and related conditions, like complications of one disease that affect another organ or body system. What information can be picked up depends on how long the person has been dead; standard appearances of organs can change once decay sets in.

- Once the organs are removed, the next step is taking tissue samples. These are processed with different chemical and staining techniques and turned into microscope slides by thin-sectioning with a device called a microtome. Because most diseases happen on the cell and tissue level, this tissue exam, or histologic exam, is part of a routine autopsy. It might take several days for the slides to be ready for examination.

- To check for the possibility of drugs or poisons, body fluids—and maybe tissue samples—are collected for the toxicology lab. These results might take a week or more to process.

- Depending on their suspicions, the pathologist might need to have microbiology tests run on body fluids or tissues, too, to check for bacteria or viruses, although this is not routine.

- The next step in the autopsy is usually to look at the brain, which can be examined in place and then removed for sectioning. Brain tissue is tricky in a couple of ways: First, prion diseases like the new variant of Creutzfeldt-Jakob disease, related to mad cow disease, are completely incurable and 100% fatal, so there is more danger to the pathologist. Second, brain tissue needs to be processed differently for thin-sectioning and microscopy, which takes more time and can delay the results of an autopsy. Brain slides are often sent to a specific specialist, called a neuropathologist.

- In some cases, the pathologist may open up the skin of the arms and legs to look for bruising or blunt trauma damage that might not be easily seen on the surface or in X-rays.

- After the autopsy is complete and all tissue and fluid samples are taken, the pathologist steps aside and the morgue attendants close up the body. The organs that were removed are usually put in a plastic bag and set in the body cavity so the corpse does not look deflated, but the organs are not put back in their anatomical positions.

After the Autopsy

- Once the remains are no longer needed for the death investigation, the coroner or medical examiner's office will release the body and any personal effects that came in with it to the funeral home designated by the next of kin. If there is no next of kin, the office decides how long to hold the body and how to respectfully dispose of the remains.

- Coroners, medical examiners, and pathologists often deal with family members as they continue the death investigation process. The family might be able to provide the victim's medical history and point the team to the hospital or doctor's office where the records might be found.

- A family member might even be called in to view and identify the body. The family could be asked about tissue donation, because some things like corneas, bone, and skin may be able to be used for a transplant even hours after death.

- The family only has so much say in the autopsy process because, by law, an autopsy can be ordered whether the family likes it or not. Some religious groups do not allow autopsy, and they can petition to prevent one, but ultimately it is up to the authorities to accept or overrule their request.

Suggested Reading

Hanzlick, *Death Investigation*.

Molina, *Handbook of Forensic Toxicology for Medical Examiners*.

Nuland, *How We Die*.

1. What is the difference between a coroner, a medical examiner, and a pathologist?

2. What types of deaths require an autopsy?

3. What is the difference between the cause of death and the manner of death?

4. Can you name the 5 possible manners of death?

5. What are the typical steps of an autopsy?

Decomposition—From Bugs to Bones
Lecture 22

The process of decomposition often leads insects, arthropods, animals, and even plant life to use the deceased body as a nutrient source. Insect life cycles, in particular, allow forensic etymologists to determine time of death. In cases where a body has been lost or dumped in a remote area, forensics experts can use these factors to help discover where the remains rest.

Nature's Garbagemen

- Climate is the major factor controlling the rate of decay. Bodies decay slowly or not at all in very low temperatures but differently in high temperatures, and the type of decay differs in moist and dry environments.

- Many life forms also contribute to decay by feeding off the dead body. Bacteria begin the process, followed quickly by insects, then animals—including both wild animals and pets. Fungi and plants can also participate in decomposition.

- While death is not a pretty process, from a scientific and practical perspective, these creatures are valuable because they act as nature's garbagemen, breaking down and removing the dead organisms that would otherwise cover the earth. They were the world's original recyclers; every single atom and molecule in our bodies is borrowed from this earth. Organisms of decomposition move chemicals around in the ecosystem and make them available for new uses.

Sarcophagic Insects

- Insects that are attracted to decomposition, called sarcophagic (or flesh-eating) insects, are actually looking for a moist, dark, nutrient-rich environment where they can deposit their eggs. Forensic entomologists are specialists who use what they know about such insects—as well as spiders and arthropods—to aid medicolegal investigations.

- Flies are usually only active during daylight, so if a body is deposited in the environment at night, it will probably be morning before the first eggs are laid. The act of laying eggs—or ovapositioning—is usually done in any body orifice, but flies will be attracted to any break in the skin, so a mass of eggs or newly hatched larvae might indicate a location where trauma occurred, like a gunshot or knife wound. Unfortunately, these insects quickly alter the original margin of the wound, complicating the pathologist's examination.

- The first stage in fly development is the larval stage. The larvae, or maggots, actually consume the corpse. As they feed and grow, they go through 3 growth phases, called instars. In the third instar stage, the larvae stop eating and will, if they can, move away from the body to somewhere cool and dark to pupate. Outdoors, this might be soil; inside a building, this might be a rug or folds in the victim's clothing or bedding.

- In the pupal stage, the outer integument of the larvae hardens into a shell called a pupa. Then the DNA directs the larval body to completely reorganize itself into an adult fly, similar to the way a caterpillar changes to a butterfly within a cocoon.

- The timing of the life stages relates to the type of fly and the environmental conditions, but for example, at 70°F (21°C), one species of blowfly egg reaches the first instar stage in about a day, the second instar stage a little over a day later, and the third instar stage by the next day. Migration and pupal case formation take another 5 days, and then metamorphosis into an adult fly will last about 6 days. So, the total time from laid egg to adult fly is a little more than 2 weeks.

- Because flies have such a scheduled life, scientists have learned to use them to help figure out how long a person has been dead. Through controlled studies, entomologists have figured out how to best collect and preserve insects on a corpse and use them, in conjunction with temperature data and information about how the conditions in which the body was kept, to develop mathematical equations used in approximating the time since death.

- Although flies are usually first, beetles start to feed on a corpse shortly thereafter. Some adult beetles do use the corpse as food; these are often called carrion beetles. Their larvae look significantly different from fly maggots and are easy to distinguish. Other insects and arthropods that might be gathered at a corpse include wasps, bees, mites, spiders, centipedes, and many more. Sometimes ants transporting fly eggs away from a body to their colony, and sometimes spiders set up webs near a corpse to catch the new flies.

Environmental Factors

- The general rule of thumb is that flies are more active when the body is in the early stages of decomposition and still has a high water content, while beetles prefer the dryer stages of decay. But there is a great deal of the variability involved in the decomposition process because environmental conditions can vary so much.

- Bodies can mummify if they desiccate in hot, dry environments, cold environments, and anywhere conditions are reasonably stable year-round, like deep within caves. Bodies can mummify or even remain fresh for a long period of time under conditions where insects cannot get to the remains. Bodies also decompose differently in water because different types of bacteria and microscopic life live there.

- Under normal conditions of exposure, in a temperate climate with 4 distinct seasons, a full-sized, adult body can fully decompose in as little as 2 weeks.

The Body Farm
- Bass Anthropology Research Facility at The University of Tennessee in Knoxville, commonly called the Body Farm, was started in the late 1980s by forensic anthropologist Dr. William Bass. There, state-of-the-art technology and simple scientific observation are used to conduct formal studies on the science of decomposition.

- The Body Farm started as an acre of ground with a 16-square-foot paved and fenced-in area in its center, where a donated body could be placed and observed while it decayed. Over the past 20 years, the facility has grown to 2.5 acres. They currently receive about 120 donated bodies a year that serve forensic science in a couple of different ways.

- Their first and foremost aim is to help us better understand the decomposition process to help forensics experts in the field come up with better time since death assessments in their work. To that end, the facility has simulated a wide variety of realistic settings that simulate how bodies may be disposed of or deposited in the environment.

- A second major way in which they have aided forensic science is by systematically analyzing the skeletal remains that are left after their decomposition studies. Their work has led to new and improved ways to assess the age, sex, ethnicity, and stature of unknown persons.

Finding Scattered Remains
- Dr. Marci Sorg has conducted studies on how large carnivores consume and scatter pig carcasses in remote parts of the Northeast United States, while Dr. Bill Haglund, has done extensive research on how remains are transported by water in Washington state.

Together, they have produced a couple of edited volumes on taphonomy—the study of what happens to the remains of organisms when they are left to the natural environment.

- When thinking of crime scenes, most people probably think of alleyways, buildings, cars, and so forth. However, many crime-scene investigations take place outside in more remote locations. If a person is murdered in New York City, the body might be tripped over by someone the next morning, but in smaller jurisdictions with low population density, bodies can fully decompose long before they are found.

- Many forensic anthropology cases have been accidentally discovered by someone and reported to police; other times, clues or tips have led investigators to believe a body might be dumped or buried in a certain area.

- In searches for scattered remains or clandestine graves, we use standard search techniques, like line searches and grid patterns, to recover remains or exclude certain areas as being free of bones or other evidence, so it helps to know what to look for in the environment.

  o When a 150-pound body decomposes in the soil, it can be like dumping 150 pounds of fertilizer in one spot. Sometimes the vegetation in the area over the grave will be taller or more green and lush than the plants growing around it.

  o If the grave is fairly recent, there may be new, early growth just taking hold on the disturbed soil.

  o There may be some trampled and broken plants around the grave, not only from the footprints of the criminals, but also from the spot where they piled the dirt they took out of the ground when they were digging the hole.

- The soil on the surface of the grave will be different from the areas around it. Soil probes let the forensic anthropologist feel around and detect the differences.

- A shallow depression might indicate a gravesite because soft tissues have decomposed and the soil has settled into what was once the victim's body cavities.

- High-tech methods can be used in certain geographic areas—including metal detectors to find jewelry, metal fasteners on clothing, or other artifacts with it, or more sophisticated devices like ground-penetrating radar. But these have limitations; for example, ground-penetrating radar can only be used on relatively flat surfaces free of trees and will detect any type of disruption in the soil, not specifically a body.

- Cadaver dogs, to date, have shown limited success in finding remains. Hopefully, training will be improved in the future.

Suggested Reading

Bass and Jefferson, *Death's Acre*.

Gennard, *Forensic Entomology*.

Goff, *A Fly for the Prosecution*.

Haglund and Sorg, eds., *Advances in Forensic Taphonomy*.

———, *Forensic Taphonomy*.

Tibbett and Carter, *Soil Analysis in Forensic Taphonomy*.

Questions to Consider

1. What are the major factors that determine whether and how decomposition occurs?

2. What types of living organisms are involved in the decomposition process?

3. What is forensic entomology?

4. How do forensic investigators search for human remains in the environment?

Forensic Anthropology—Skeleton Stories
Lecture 23

orensic anthropologists use their knowledge of the human skeleton to assist in death investigations in multiple ways. Their jobs are to establish the biological profile of human remains—that is, the age, sex, ancestry, and stature—as well as look for evidence of trauma or disease in the skeleton. Being able to distinguish between postmortem, antemortem, and perimortem abnormalities can sometimes help establish a cause of death.

Forensic Anthropology

- Anthropology is the study of humans in all our manifestations, and so covers several different subfields. The 4 main fields are linguistics, cultural (or social) anthropology, archaeology, and physical anthropology.

- Physical anthropology looks at humanity through our physicality, our relationship to other primates, our evolution, and our bodies—past and present—with special emphasis on the skeleton, since its durability links us to that past.

- Modern physical anthropology studies blood types, human biological adaptation to the environment, genetics, and ancient and modern DNA. Particularly in the last half of the 20th century, physical anthropologists have also stepped into the realm of forensic science.

- Forensic anthropologists typically examine human remains that may relate to legal questions. Once bones are established to be human, the next question a forensic anthropologist addresses is whether or not the bones are of forensic significance.

The Anthropological Autopsy

- Modern construction often turns up human bones that are prehistoric or early historic, and it takes a trained eye to recognize the context, the heavily worn teeth, and the bone qualities that point to really old remains. Some high-tech methods, like radiocarbon dating, can be used to approximate the age of bones, but most of the time anthropologists rely on years of training and experience.

- The next responsibility of a forensic anthropologist is to establish the age, sex, ancestry, and stature of the remains. Together, we call those things the biological profile. The ability to figure out those things depends a lot on the condition of the remains. It is easier to generate a biological profile from a full skeleton from a few isolated bones, a single bone, or just a bone fragment.

- A forensic anthropologist performs a nontraditional autopsy. They examine remains when there is not enough of a body left to make the typical examination. These include skeletons, mummified remains, isolated body parts, and badly burned or cremated remains.

- In cases where the body is in some intermediate stage of decay, forensic anthropologists have their own special recipes for processing the remains, often involving large Crock-Pots, detergents, and other ways to slowly simmer off soft tissue without using anything sharp that could introduce additional trauma to the bones.

- Forensic anthropologists look for other key indicators of individuality and anything in the skeleton that could be related to stress or injury. They can also help determine the number of people involved in a mass fatality if the remains are fragmentary and commingled as well as taphonomic changes that can help estimate the postmortem interval.

- In the morgue, anthropologists often work side-by-side with pathologists to interpret bone trauma—either directly or through X-rays. They may reconstruct fragmentary remains to get a better look at features related to trauma or identity. They may need to examine associated artifacts, such as weapons, to see if they match trauma sites.

- Lastly, the forensic anthropologist must prepare a formal report to submit to the agency in charge of the investigation. This is especially important in case the anthropologist needs to testify in court.

Assessing Skeletal Age

- You may have been taught that there are 206 bones in the human body. In fact, that is an average; that number is only true for normal adults—not the skeletons of fetuses, children, and sometimes not older folks. In general, we go from having many bones to fewer bones throughout our lifetime. The numbers change over time because of the way bones form, mature, and degenerate.

- The skeleton of a newborn shows the same general pattern as the adult skeleton, but the dimensions and shapes of the bones are different. The skull and eye sockets, in particular, are proportionally much larger because we are born with a bigger brain-to-body ratio.

- Babies are born with the soft spots, called fontanels, in their skulls, where some of the bones of the braincase are not yet fully formed. After the soft spots close up, they leave joints called sutures. These often persist throughout life, but in some geriatrics, the sutures fuse completely, so technically an older person does not have 206 bones anymore. The same would hold true if arthritis fuses the vertebrae of the spine or joints in the hands and feet.

- Different bones develop differently: The clavicle, or collarbone, more or less just gets bigger in size throughout development without really changing its shape much. But the long bones of the body, like those in the arms and legs, show pretty dramatic changes.

- A long bone begins its development as a stick-like cartilage precursor. The cartilage of the major long bones of the fetal limbs start to turn to bone, or ossify, at about 7 weeks of development.

- By birth, the newborn humerus or femur is a shaft of bone that is capped on either end with a knob of cartilage. Later in childhood, the cartilage margins start to ossify, too. The bony knobs are connected to the shaft by cartilaginous zones called growth plates. When a bone reaches its genetically determined adult length—and that varies for different people, and is affected by health and nutrition—the growth plate will seal up. So a child technically has more bones—or at least bony elements—than adults do.

- Although there is a bit of individual variation, there are general patterns of growth plate closure. Plates around the elbows seal up first, next the ones near the hips, then the ankles, knees, wrists, and finally those around the shoulders. The last growth plate that usually closes up is the one at the central end of the clavicle, around 23 to 25 years of age.

- Assessing age in a child's skeleton can also be done from their teeth, which is sometimes more reliable than skeletal changes. Tooth development seems to be slightly less influenced by malnutrition and other health factors than bone development.

- Therefore, using a combination of visual observations and X-rays, and by examining both teeth and bones, a good physical anthropologist can usually do a pretty decent job of narrowing down the age of a child. We can often come within months for fetuses and newborns, but the range might span a couple of years by the time a child reaches the toddler age. In kids who are older, that range may spread to a few more years.

- Once the skeleton is finished growing—in our early 20s—age assessments are based on degenerational changes. In adult skeletons, anthropologists look for things like arthritis and bone mineral loss, although the individual's activity level affects both factors, so these do not follow strict age-related patterns.

- Some of the best evidence for an adult skeleton's age can be found in places you might never consider. A joint in the front of the pelvis between the right and left hipbones called the pubic symphysis goes through some characteristic age-related changes, probably related to the biomechanics of walking. The ends of the ribs, where they meet the sternum, show characteristic age changes as well.

- Anthropologists' observations have generated standards that we can compare to skeletons where the age is unknown, but the methods are not perfect. Once you add in the standard deviations, you are often left with a broad age estimate—sometimes a 30 or 40 year spread—on an adult skeleton.

Assessing Skeletal Sex and Ethnicity

- While age assessment in children is relatively easy, it is impossible to tell whether skeletal remains come from a little boy or little girl, without DNA testing. Before puberty, the skeletons of boys and girls are generic with regard to sex. On the other hand, adult remains usually show good evidence of whether they belonged to a male or female.

- One of the best places to look in the skeleton to judge sex is the pelvis. At puberty, under the influence of hormones, the female pelvis gets wider from side to side and from front to back. This is in preparation for childbirth—specifically, because of the large skulls that human babies have.

Anthropologists are sometimes asked to compare the photographs of living people to a skull of questioned identity.

- The skull can show some pretty clear sex differences. Males often have a brow ridge that sticks out further, and females usually have a higher and smoother forehead. Men usually have a more squared chin and jaw, while women's are more pointed.

- Males typically have more robust and rugged muscle attachment sites on their bones than females do. Even if their bones are exactly the same length, a man's will have a larger joint surface.

Testosterone produces larger and sturdier bones on average, as well as bigger joints.

- In court, an anthropologist cannot simply testify that a skeleton looked male or female. Therefore, mathematical equations have been developed based on measurements taken on the bones of people known to be male or female that can be compared to bones in question.

- These same types of mathematical formulas have been developed to assess stature and ancestry—the latter being the most complicated part of a skeletal analysis. There are some dimensions between certain landmarks on the skull, particularly in the mid-face region, that tend to differ among people whose ancestry comes from different parts of the world.

- Mathematical formulas have been developed for these as well, but you need a pretty intact skull to use them, and the methods are complicated by the fact that more and more modern people have more and more diverse ancestry.

Trauma Analysis
- Unless you really look very closely, you might not realize that there are a lot of little nooks and crannies in bones. Sometimes it takes a well-trained eye to figure out what is supposed to be there and what is not. When trauma is found, it can be really important to establish roughly when it occurred.

  o Antemortem trauma refers to things that happened before a person died—like a pre-existing and healed fracture or evidence of some chronic bone disease—that probably do not relate to the cause of death but they can be clues about an unknown person's identity.

  o Postmortem trauma involves things that damage bones after death, like when buried remains are accidentally discovered by a construction crew.

- Perimortem trauma is bone damage that happened at or around the time of death and may be related to the cause or manner of death.

- The perimortem interval is usually ill-defined, and there are only so many ways a person can die that will show up in bone. For example, if a decomposing body is found in a well, and the investigator sees a fracture in the jaw, can he or she really say that happened at death, or did it happen after, when the body was thrown down the well? The one exception to this rule is the hyoid bone, which is often broken during strangulation.

Suggested Reading

Bass and Jefferson, *Death's Acre*.

Craig, *Teasing Secrets from the Dead*.

Haglund and Sorg, eds., *Advances in Forensic Taphonomy*.

———, *Forensic Taphonomy*.

Maples and Browning, *Dead Men Do Tell Tales*.

Scammell and Ubelaker, *Bones*.

Steadman, *Hard Evidence*.

Tibbett and Carter, *Soil Analysis in Forensic Taphonomy*.

White and Folkens, *The Human Bone Manual*.

Questions to Consider

1. What types of biological or demographic features can a forensic anthropologist glean about a person from his or her skeletal remains?

2. How do bones change throughout human growth and development?

3. Can the visual examination of the bones of a child suggest whether the child was male or female?

4. What types of technology does a forensic anthropologist use in the analysis of skeletal remains?

Forensics of Teeth and Bite Marks

Lecture 24

F orensic odontology has 2 major branches. The first and most common is to establish positive identity through discerning the unique features of an individual's teeth. This can include their age and health in general, as well as narrowing down a specific identity through unique damage and dental work. Bite-mark analysis, the second branch, is an important and interesting area of forensic odontology that continues to be researched and used in casework.

Forensic Dentistry

- Forensic pathologists focus fairly strictly on people who have died; the same is largely true of forensic anthropologists. But forensic odontologists—dentists trained to use their knowledge of human teeth to help identify unknown persons and to interpret bite-mark evidence— have one foot in the world of the dead and another in the land of the living.

- Teeth are even more durable than bones and—like bones—are sources of information throughout all stages of life, as well as after death. Also, because many people regularly visit a dentist for a variety of treatments—like fillings and other restorations, bridges, and implants— dental therapy results in unique features in many of us.

- One of the most infamous cases where forensic odontology was used to seal the deal on an investigation was that of Ted Bundy. The forensic dentists at Bundy's trial had several things going for them:

    o First, Bundy had some unique features in his dentition;

    o second, he had bitten a particular victim, Lisa Levy, twice in about the same location—once in one direction, and then a second bite almost perpendicular to the first—giving them 2 sources of some pretty compelling evidence.

o   Third, Levy—like so many of Bundy's other casualties—was apparently attacked first, and then sexually assaulted afterward—and we will see that the victim's condition is just as important as the attacker's bite.

The Anatomy of Teeth

- Like fingerprints, the dental pattern in each of us is unique—even between identical twins. This is because both genetic and environmental factors shape tooth development.

- Each tooth is composed of an exposed crown and an embedded root, with a neck in between the two. The root of each tooth is anchored in a socket, or alveolus. The upper jaw is called the maxilla, and the lower jaw is the mandible. Connective tissues called periodontal ligaments and a biological binder known as cementum help hold each tooth root in its socket.

- The outer covering of enamel on the tooth's crown is the hardest native substance in the body. This covers a bonelike core of living tissue called dentin, which contain an inner chamber called the pulp cavity and its extensions called root canals, which house the nerves and blood vessels associated with each tooth.

- Humans get 2 sets of teeth during their lifetimes: Primary baby teeth, sometimes called deciduous teeth, and secondary adult teeth, sometimes called permanent teeth. Primary teeth begin development at 6 weeks in utero and then start to mineralize by 14 weeks of fetal age. They typically erupt between 6 months and 2.5 years of age. By around age 6 or 7, baby teeth usually begin to be shed and permanent teeth start to erupt.

- Humans, like other mammals, are known as heterodonts; that means we have different tooth types in our mouth. There are usually 20 primary teeth, fully erupted in a child's mouth by about age 3, plus or minus a year, including 4 incisors, 2 canines, and 4 molars in each jaw. There are typically between 28 and 32 permanent teeth, depending on whether or not the third molars, commonly called wisdom teeth, develop. This includes 4 incisors, 2 canines, 4 premolars, and 4–6 molars in each jaw.

- Permanent teeth start to form soon after birth. Typically, the 6-year molars erupt first behind the baby teeth. The permanent tooth crown formation in the front part of the jaws then destabilizes the baby teeth, causing them to shed. Their roots break down and are reabsorbed by the body, and the crowns become unstable and are lost, which is scientifically known as exfoliation.

- Because the standard ages of tooth development and eruption patterns have been so well documented, they allow pretty good scientific age estimations through visual exams and X-rays. Anthropologists trained to estimate age from teeth use these methods not only in forensic casework but when looking at historic or prehistoric remains from archaeology sites. There are also occasions when teeth are used to help determine the age of a living child.

Environmental Effects on Teeth

- Within these fairly standard patterns, there is also some individual variation—not only in tooth development and eruption times, but in the structure of teeth, as well. All these similarities and differences are due to a combination of genetic and environmental factors.

- Linear enamel hypoplasias are horizontal lines that form in the tooth enamel and are thought to reflect bodily stresses in kids, like from weaning or childhood diseases. Cavities—also known as dental caries— are environmental effects that result when acids from bacteria eat away at tooth enamel. Some people seem to have stronger enamel than others, but sugary diets and poor dental care are huge factors in tooth decay.

- Other chemicals affect tooth formation, like the permanent yellow, gray, and/or brown enamel staining that can affect developing teeth when the antibiotic tetracycline is given to children and even the growing baby teeth of fetuses if a pregnant woman takes tetracycline.

- Elements from a person's diet, especially minerals from groundwater, get incorporated into teeth during their development and become a permanent record within each tooth. Forensic scientists have tried to identify where an unknown person may have lived as a child by looking at tooth chemistry, though this is seldom used.

- Tooth grinding, or bruxism, can cause tooth wear that can be fairly distinctive. Even hobbies can alter teeth, for example in people who use their teeth like tools, say when sewing or using a pipe.

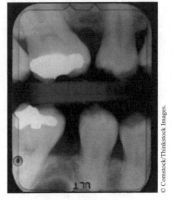

© Comstock/Thinkstock Images.

- Tooth wear can also give clues about a person's age. If their third molars, or wisdom teeth, are well-worn, it usually means the person is quite a bit older than 30 or so.

In cases of questioned identity, dental records of a suspected person can be compared to those of an unknown dead person.

- A big part of what makes one person's teeth much more different from another's involves modifications done at a dental or orthodontic office or accidental chips in teeth that are not repaired.

- When a tooth is lost, its alveolar socket closes up in about 6 months. If a forensic odontologist sees a healing alveolus in a jaw, they know the person had a tooth extracted or lost a tooth fairly recently.

Dental Records and Identification
- Aesthetic modifications in both historical and modern cultures, like decorative implants and filing, can be other clues to someone's identity. Medical restorations like fillings and restorations are pretty unique, too, especially given the number of teeth, the variety of places that can be worked on, and the variety of materials that can be used to fill teeth.

- Orthodontic work often leaves behind a tooth cast sitting in storage somewhere from the person who once wore the braces. The same is true for the X-rays of teeth that are commonplace recordkeeping in any dental practice. These records can be used for identification in the event a person goes missing and investigators later want to compare the dental records of the missing person to an unidentified person in a morgue.

Bite-mark Evidence

- The first bite-mark evidence used in a criminal prosecution occurred during the Salem Witch Hunts of 1692, when Reverend George Burroughs was accused and convicted of biting a woman's wrist, despite being in jail at the time of the attack.

- In 1952, in the case *Doyle v. Texas*, a man was found guilty of burglary after his dental pattern was linked to a half-eaten piece of cheese he left behind at the scene. Between the 1970s and the 1990s, bite-mark evidence was at its heyday in legal systems around the world.

- Several forensic odontology organizations sprang up in America and elsewhere, and among their many important contributions, they generated an increased awareness of bite marks as indicators of abuse—especially in child and elder abuse and cases of domestic violence.

- In the past decade or so, however, bite marks are among the many types of forensic evidence that have come under increasing scrutiny. Like lots of other scientific techniques used in forensics, there is a measure of subjectivity to bite-mark analysis that cannot be overlooked. More work must be done to standardize bite-mark evidence, or limit its use in legal issues.

- Bite-mark investigation attempts to link living perpetrators to victims not only in homicides but also in abuse cases, sexual assaults, and animal attacks on both the living and dead. Almost nobody dies from being bitten, with the exception of bites from venomous creatures, but even nonlethal bites can still be pretty damaging, and may lead to infection and severe scarring, maybe even loss of function.

- Both fatal and nonfatal bites can range from obvious to very subtle, so to investigate a bite mark, first it has to be recognized as such. The anatomy of skin causes unpredictable distortion. Because of this, bite-mark evidence on a body will vary in a number of ways, including where the victim is bit, whether or not they resist, whether the victim is dead or alive, and the force used by the biter.

- Areas of skin overlying muscle and connective tissues generally retain bite-mark patterns better than areas of skin over fatty areas. The more the victim is moving, the less distinct the bite will be, because there are active forces working in 2 different directions if the victim struggles against the perpetrator.

- Biting someone after death leaves a better pattern than when a living person is bitten. Living tissue reacts to a bite with inflammation, like swelling, and people will usually treat a bite immediately, even if just to rub the area.

- Evidence on a living victim needs to be examined within about 8 hours after the attack, and hopefully before it has been treated. The wound should be photographed right away and then rephotographed repeatedly over about a week.

- Most people think that the more pressure applied, the more distinctive the mark will be. But actually, the harder the bite, the less distinct the impression is because aggressive bites leave bruising and may tear tissues—making it tough to see a pattern. Multiple bites in the same spot can also complicate analysis if they are superimposed on each other.

- Pathologists can also use bite-mark evidence and other skin injuries in the morgue to help establish the time since death. In the case of an antemortem attack—remember, that means before death— there will usually be more diffuse bruising, because blood is still circulating. A bite made within about 5 minutes of death causes much more well-defined bruising. But a postmortem bite will leave defined indentations and no bruising at all because circulation has stopped.

- A typical bite mark will be more or less circular or oval and made up of 2 curved arches that face each other. When the biter stops, the skin's elastic properties will return it to its original position unless a whole chunk of tissue gets torn off.

- Bites do not always have that double arch appearance, especially on a finger, toe, or other projecting body part. When there is clothing, hair, or something else over the skin, it can act like a cushion and protect the skin from all or part of a bite. That can leave a mark that looks like just one arch or just one side of the mouth.

- Usually, the pattern in a human bite mark shows between 6 and 12 individual tooth marks (though there can be up to 16)—8 from the upper jaw and 8 from the lower. Mostly front teeth are involved.

- Different tooth types make different marks: Incisors make rectangles; canines make triangular or circular marks. The marks are usually bigger for upper teeth compared to their lower partners.

- Other pattern injuries can mimic a bite mark, like the heel of a shoe or an animal hoof mark. Even the fungal infection ringworm can occasionally look like a bite mark.

- As with other types of impression evidence, bite-mark specialists often use alternate light source photography to enhance patterns. Ultraviolet light does not penetrate the skin, so ultraviolet photography can show good surface detail, like indentations and abrasions.

- Because melanin absorbs ultraviolet light, ultraviolet photographs can show changes in skin color not visible to the unaided eye. In fact, "healed" bite marks can often be seen months after the initial injury using ultraviolet photography. Infrared light penetrates a few millimeters into the skin and can be used to show bruising in deeper tissues, which can be especially helpful if the victim has dark skin.

- Photographs of bite marks—or other patterned injuries on a living victim—need to continue to be taken over time because the bite-mark pattern can sometimes appear more clearly over time than it was at the initial attack.

- A fresh bite mark should also be swabbed for other evidence, like salivary enzymes, ABO blood typing, DNA, and even microbes because the bacteria in people's mouths differ, and so do the bacterial populations of nonhuman animals.

- Investigators should also consider the victim's own dental pattern, too, because self-inflicted bite marks are not out of the question. If the bite mark is on a person in the morgue, it can actually be excised along with the surrounding skin, and preserved in formalin to stop decomposition.

Suggested Reading

Bowers, ed., *Forensic Dental Evidence*.

Libal, *Fingerprints, Bite Marks, Ear Prints*.

Senn and Stimson, *Forensic Dentistry*.

Questions to Consider

1. What is a forensic odontologist?

2. How do teeth vary among people, and how is this information used in forensic science?

3. Is forensic dentistry used on the living as well as on the dead?

Police Sketches and Facial Reproductions
Lecture 25

Forensic artists use a combination of art and science in their work, and—like odontologists—they commonly work with both the dead and the living. Forensic art is surprisingly interdisciplinary because in addition to being skilled artists, its practitioners need to understand some human biology—such as the anatomy and growth of facial bones and other tissues of the face throughout a person's lifetime. Forensic artists also have to use some principles of psychology when they participate in witness interviews, and they need to understand the legal context of their work.

Forensic Art and Forensic Artists

- Forensic artists come from a variety of backgrounds and training, and technology has significantly changed the way they work over time, but one thing has never changed: A good forensic artist must be a keen observer of human physical traits.

- Forensic art is often used to trigger recognition—for example, when police are searching for someone. Age-progression images, especially for missing children, are also attempts to trigger recognition in someone who might know where that missing person is.

- Artists can also clean up morgue photos and make them more presentable so that they can be released to the media. In addition, when severely traumatic injuries disfigure a victim's face, a forensic artist can sometimes reconfigure the features to try to reproduce the person's antemortem appearance.

- Forensic artists are sometimes recruited to enhance images rather than actual faces, such as pictures from surveillance tapes that might be grainy or shadowed. Because of their extensive knowledge of facial anatomy, forensic artists may be asked to compare images between a surveillance recording and a photograph of a suspect, for example.

- Another responsibility that is taken on by some forensic artists is to prepare demonstrative evidence for presentation in the courtroom. For example, an artist might create an aerial view of a large crime scene or develop a computer animation that shows how an accident most likely happened.

- Over the years, there have been many changes in forensic art technology, and what began with simple 2-dimensional images has now gone digital. Today, flat images are often generated electronically, using computer software technologies. A commercial product called Identi-Kit even produces police sketches based on witness statements.

- Three-dimensional facial reconstructions essentially create a sculpted bust from clay of an unknown person from his or her skull. They're remarkable but also very time consuming.

- More recently, facial reconstructions from skulls are being done using computer technology, where high-quality images of the skull taken from several angles are put into a computer. Like other computer-generated images, they're not only faster—and, therefore, less expensive—but also can be easily tweaked.

Anatomy and Geometry of Human Skulls

- Some people have rounder heads, and some people have heads that are more long and narrow. The basic shape of our skull is largely determined by genetics, and because of that, there are ancestral differences—and potentially racial differences—among head shapes. It's not the job of the forensic artist to label people, but rather to interpret a likeness.

- Anthropologists have studied human remains for centuries. One focus has been to better understand the anatomy behind the diversity that's seen in skull shape and facial geometry and then to classify the differences observed. This research has been done using skulls of known ancestry that have been extensively measured by anthropologists and statistically analyzed.

- Because human groups emanate from 3 basic ancestral stocks, each of which spent long periods of genetic isolation in different parts of the world, there are 3 standard ancestral groups: African derived (Negroid), European derived (Caucasoid), and Asian derived (Mongoloid). Aboriginal people, who are indigenous to Australia, don't really fit into the 3-part scheme.

- Whether a forensic artist is working from a skull or constructing a sketch of a suspect based on a witness account, the artist needs to have a good working knowledge of the typical head shapes and facial features that characterize people whose family trees grew in different parts of the world.

Head Shape and Facial Features

- There are 2 major areas of the skull: the braincase, which is scientifically called the cranium, and the facial region. These 2 subunits change their proportions pretty drastically during childhood development.

- There are few, if any, bony changes in the skull associated with aging once skeletal growth is complete, but if someone loses all of their teeth—which could happen at any age, especially in the case of an accident—the mandible can change its proportions and somewhat alter a person's facial geometry.

- A forensic artist needs to understand changes in soft-tissue anatomy as a person ages because he or she will have to generate a reconstruction or sketch based on the subject's general age category.

- There are also differences between male and female skulls that can be pretty strong in some men and women, but other people have relatively ambiguous traits and show little sexual dimorphism. The degree of sexual dimorphism seems to vary among ethnic groups.

- When considering any of these patterns in skulls—ancestry traits, growth and development, or sexual dimorphism—the underlying bone structure plays a big role in a person's facial appearance, but so do their soft tissues.

- Cadavers of people of known race, age, and sex have been historically studied in order to quantify the average tissue thicknesses overlying certain bony landmarks on the skull. This research has also helped to discover the typical dimensions of structures such as the nose, ears, and other facial features.

- More recently, CT scans and MRIs of living people have been used, instead of cadavers, because they not only allow more diverse population groups to be studied—including younger people and children—but they also are not affected by any postmortem tissue changes.

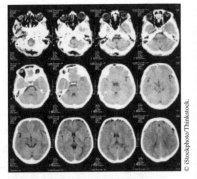

© iStockphoto/Thinkstock.

Forensic Age Progression
- The techniques for age progression developed out of the need to help find children who are missing on a long-term basis, such as children abducted by noncustodial parents or teenagers who run away.

X-rays, CT scans, and MRIs document the changes in cranial and facial proportions as human skulls develop.

- The methods behind age progression were developed by 2 medical illustrators named Scott Barrows and Lewis Sadler and were based on pediatric research about the development of skulls and faces of children.

- Techniques for age progressions have included both conventional sketching and computerized technology; the choice of which to use often depends on what kind of existing photos are available.

- Some age-progression experts tend to put a lot of emphasis on changes seen in other family members over time—and, therefore, use parent and sibling images to help develop age progressions—but other experts think scientific data on growth should outweigh family resemblances.

- Age progression isn't just used for children; it can also be used to update the face of a long-term missing adult or fugitive. This is also done from photographs—either by hand or using a computer.

- Because there are so many variables in the genetic, environmental, and physical stresses that affect people as they age, a good forensic artist will often produce a few different age progressions of the same adult to capture the range of possible variations—especially for things that are known to differ among people.

- Because the same principles of variation apply to facial reproductions from skulls, a forensic artist should use his or her expertise and what's known about the victim to generate the reconstruction—but either leave generic what might be unknown or present multiple views as possibilities.

- When it comes to helping apprehend suspects after a crime, forensic artists have additional challenges that take them far beyond their artwork. In these situations, they not only have to create the face of a living fugitive, but they also have to gather the information for that image from a living witness.

Police Sketch Artists

- When listening to eyewitness accounts, a police sketch artist needs to realize that the image he or she produces is based on the fallible nature of human memory.

- Police sketches are more technically known as composite images, which help convey the fact that they're collective images made up by individually described parts, such as noses, lips, and eyes.

- These composite images are also a collection of visual memories from one or more people who saw the suspect or perpetrator during what might be a very tense and intense event—the commission of a crime.

- In order to gather these recollections, forensic artists need to have good interviewing skills, including an understanding of memory and the way trauma affects it. Their goal is a quality likeness of the subject with an emphasis on forensics—not just an artistic drawing of someone's face.

- Psychological studies demonstrate that people can recognize things easier than they can recall them, meaning that it's easier for us to recognize someone we know than to describe their face. Some photo queues of specific features might be helpful, but the images that a witness is shown may blur their memory.

Recommendations for Sketch Artists

- The sketch artist should sit off to the side of the witness so that the witness doesn't get confused by seeing the sketch artist's face during the interview. There also shouldn't be any pictures of human faces around that the witness could inadvertently pull facial features from as they're describing the suspect.

- The artist should start with open-ended questions and then later focus on details. A good artist will know how to use average features for the appropriate ancestry to cover any details that the witness doesn't feel confident about.

- The artist also shouldn't sketch where the witness has full or direct view of the drawing; it should be as complete as possible before it is shown to the witness.

- Really valuable information might include things like scars, marks, and tattoos because these set individuals apart from the crowd. Head and facial hair can be added if details of color, length, shape, and texture are given.

- For reproducing hats and glasses the suspect might have worn, it helps for the artist to have a photo book with examples that the witness can pick from. Facial expressions can also be captured by the forensic artist if the witness makes mention of them.

- After the initial sketch is completed, the witness should be asked to look at it, and then more structured questions should be used to fine-tune the drawing.

- The artist does not want to encourage fabrication because of pressure or praise—which is especially true when interviewing children.

- Interviewing for forensic art isn't the same as a police interview; an artist's interview is much more of a cognitive interview—not just a collection of facts.

- At the conclusion of the interview and facial reproduction, the artist needs to sign and date the work in case it ends up as evidence in court.

- Research has shown that many artists can often subconsciously incorporate their own facial features in their work, so it's important that artists are careful not to inadvertently incriminate themselves in their forensic art.

Suggested Reading

George, *Facial Geometry*.

Gibson, *Forensic Art Essentials*.

Taylor, *Forensic Art and Illustration*.

1. What are the major uses of artistry in forensic science?

2. Why would a forensic artist need good interviewing skills?

3. How has forensic art changed over time?

4. How is forensic art used with regard to living people versus the dead?

Interview, Interrogation, Intelligence
Lecture 26

W̶e hold a lot of information in our memories based on things we see or hear; some of it we readily divulge, but other things we tend to keep private or even conceal. In a criminal investigation, the people involved may have as much or more to say about what happened as the physical evidence, but it can be a challenge to get them to communicate their evidence. Suspects have a right against self-incrimination, and a select group of people have privileged communication—depending on their relationship to a suspect—so a refusal to speak is legally acceptable.

Types of Investigations
- Investigations can be broken down into 3 types: administrative investigations—which are fact-finding inquiries within an agency—criminal investigations, and criminal defense investigations.

- There are 3 main steps in any criminal investigation: determining whether a certain action constitutes a criminal act; figuring out who the offender is and locating him or her; and showing the connections between the offender, the victim, and the crime.

- Investigations are reactive to a complaint or action while intelligence gathering is proactive and attempts to anticipate—and hopefully prevent—illegal activity.

- When investigating a crime, authorities have to make sure that the crime occurred in their jurisdiction before they start investigating it. Police officers need to understand local, state, and federal laws and may have to connect with other agencies if a crime spans multiple jurisdictions.

- Another related task of law enforcement might be to find and recover stolen property to demonstrate criminal activity and figure out who may be responsible. Police may have to locate the property, and possibly verify ownership, in order to show that a crime occurred.

- When the police, the prosecutor's office, or the grand jury decides that criminal activity may have taken place, the formal investigative process starts. This might mean going to the courts for a search warrant if the police are just beginning to try to figure out who is responsible for a crime, but if there's enough evidence that fairly confidently points to a suspect, the police might request an arrest warrant along with the search warrant.

Interviewing Witnesses

- The term "interview" is used for people who authorities expect are willing to divulge what they know about what is—or could be—criminal activity.

- Witnesses—whether victims or not—are sources of sensory information about an event. Visual observations are the most common followed by things the witness may have heard, such as a scream, a gunshot, or something that was said. Occasionally, a witness can attest to a certain smell or taste or even something they felt.

- During any type of interview, investigators will try to cover who, what, where, when, and why. They will also want to add how— in other words, how the witness or victim believes the crime was committed.

- During any actual questioning of the interviewee, authorities have to consider such factors as the person's emotional state, vantage point, and motive for coming forward—which would certainly be different for an eyewitness looking out of her apartment window who sees a purse snatcher than for the lady whose purse was stolen.

- Not all witnesses jump at the opportunity to tell police what they may know about a crime. Reluctant witnesses might be afraid of police or scared that the perpetrator might retaliate against them—sometimes with good reason. In fact, this reluctant witness phenomenon is responsible for anonymous tip lines.

- Witnesses, or even victims, may just think that they can't afford to miss work—if talking to the police means they'll have to go before the grand jury, which could be just the beginning of what turns into a lengthy trial. In the police interview environment, anyone can refuse to talk, but victims and witnesses can be compelled to testify in grand jury and other court hearings.

- Obviously, officers have to approach reluctant witnesses differently than they would those who are completely cooperative. If confronted with victims or witnesses who refuse to speak, officers might remind them that they could be subpoenaed to give a statement in a more formal and less inviting courtroom environment, which could help alleviate their apprehension.

- Sometimes, people are actually unaware that they were a witness to a crime. Police will even canvass an area for witnesses to try to find people that might have seen a criminal or some criminal activity without even realizing it but once made aware could end up giving police an interview.

- When questioning children or those with diminished capacities—including people of limited or marginal intelligence and people whose memory is or was known to be impaired due to drugs, alcohol, or age-related memory loss—interviews require special considerations. Sometimes, an interview may happen years after a crime, such as when reinvestigating a cold case.

- Officers sometimes even give thought to the physical space in which an interview is conducted—for example, whether they want to question someone at home or at the police station. Some considerations depend on whether the person being questioned is a victim, witness, or suspect.

- When a victim is deceased, investigators might still be able to do a highly modified form of an interview called a victim profile. Victimology, which is the study of the victim, may help lead them to draw inferences about the offender, including motive or signature behaviors.

- Looking at a victim's associations—including his or her family, any pertinent financial records, or any link the victim may have to criminal activity—is very important. People on the wrong side of the law are typically far more likely to end up as the victim of crimes or in the morgue than the average law-abiding citizen.

Interrogating Suspects
- The term "interrogation" is typically reserved for the interview conducted of a suspect—rather than a victim or bystander.

- Law enforcement has to decide whether to arrest and then interrogate a person—which is called a custodial interview and allows the possibility of the suspect invoking Miranda rights— or interview first and then follow with arrest if the results of the interview warrant an arrest.

- Strategies about how to approach the suspect are important; this might even include choosing a specific investigator who is most likely to gain suspect cooperation.

- Throughout any suspect interrogation, the rights of the person being questioned must be maintained in order to ensure that the information gathered can be suitable later in a court of law, if necessary.

- In real life, an interrogation is usually conducted by only one person—not by multiple investigators at the same time and certainly not by forensic scientists, which is the way interrogations are often depicted on television

- Investigators are trained not to get harsh during an interrogation. To get the best results from the questioning, officers should speak in a soft and normal tone and try to befriend and win the confidence of the suspect.

- The goal of an interrogation is to uncover the truth, which is different than trying to get a confession; people can confess to anything and sometimes do. Law enforcement officers are not trying to trick the person being questioned in the ways you see on television.

- It is a good idea for the interrogator to spend the first 15 to 20 minutes of the interrogation just getting to know the person a little, particularly to establish their identity and to make sure that they have good mental faculties—so that they can't later say that they didn't understand what was going on during the interrogation.

An investigator should take time to learn about a person's character and background before beginning an interrogation.

- An investigator always has to consider that someone who is brought in—or even comes in—as a witness could actually be the perpetrator. However, as soon as an interview turns in that direction, the officer will either need to terminate the interview and collect more information or will have to apprise the person of their constitutional rights before continuing.

- Depending on the agency and the nature of the crime, the interview or interrogation may be—or in some jurisdictions—must be recorded in some way. Investigators may place an audio recorder on the table during a standard interview or an interrogation but may not tell the person they are also being videotaped because people tend to become much more self-conscious on videotape than audiotape.

- Criminal defense investigators (CDIs) work outside of law enforcement and are employed by other agencies, attorneys, or private clients, but they're more than what we think of when we hear the term "private investigators." Just as any other investigator, legitimate CDIs should objectively try to uncover truth and facts.

Gathering Intelligence
- Beat cops gather intelligence all the time—just by patrolling an area and observing anything that could relate to criminal activity. On a grander scale, "intelligence" typically means gathering information and using it to thwart organized crime and terrorism.

- Intelligence involves 3 key elements: assessment, integration, and deduction.

  o Assessment means to judge the significance of the information gathered, which also involves its pertinence and reliability, including the credibility of its source.

  o Integration involves putting the parts and pieces together to come up with a composite story.

  o Deduction means to figure out what this series of linked facts and events signifies—including how it can be used to predict what might happen next.

- The general public doesn't usually think of intelligence gathering as something that happens much on the local level, but intelligence is being gathered and stored daily by even the smallest departments, and local law enforcement officers from across neighboring jurisdictions meet monthly to share information.

- Narcotics agents and drug task forces are typically the largest sources of intelligence because most criminal activity has a drug connection—which is even true for national and international terrorism.

- The Regional Information Sharing Systems (RISS) is a program for the law enforcement community that began in the 1970s in the United States mainly to help control organized crime, such as drug trafficking, identity theft, human trafficking, violent crime, and terrorism. RISS allows shared intelligence using a centralized database and gives agencies access to common investigative resources and services.

- The High Intensity Drug Trafficking Areas (HIDTA) program is used to control drug trafficking. By examining both civilian and law enforcement databases, HIDTA can help find suspects and their associates and try to link them to vehicles, homes, and financial assets.

- To effectively combat terrorism, extremism, drug trafficking, and other forms of organized crime, investigators have to gather as much intelligence as possible about any significant groups or movements who are—or have the potential to become—involved in illegal acts. The law enforcement strategies used, though, still need to be carefully controlled in light of the personal rights and freedoms provided by the U.S. Constitution.

- Intelligence gathering includes all standard investigation tools—such as surveillance of suspects' activities, including communications and financial records. In some cases, law enforcement officials attempt to infiltrate criminal organizations using undercover tactics.

Suggested Reading

Eisen, Quas, and Goodman, *Memory and Suggestibility in the Forensic Interview.*

Kranacher, Riley, and Wells, *Forensic Accounting and Fraud Examination.*

Napier, *Behavior, Truth, and Deception.*

Navarro, *Hunting Terrorists.*

Peterson, *Understanding Surveillance Technologies.*

Zulawski, Wicklander, Sturman, and Hoover, *Practical Aspects of Interview and Interrogation.*

Questions to Consider

1. What is the difference between intelligence—in a forensic context—and interview?

2. How are investigative methods used to fight organized crime and terrorism?

3. What legal rights do people being interviewed or interrogated have in the United States?

Forensic Profiling—Who, How, and Why?
Lecture 27

P rofiling is one of the most controversial, and intriguing, aspects of forensic science. The word "profiling" has different meanings. It can be loosely applied as a screening tool, for example, to identify potential airline hijackers by how they look or act. It's also sometimes used in relation to traffic stops, in cases where law enforcement officers stop people because of their race or other characteristics. Sometimes this is quite legitimate—such as if a Hispanic female was just seen leaving the scene of a crime—but other times, profiling is alleged to be prejudicial.

What Is Profiling?

- Beginning in around the 1960s, the term "profiling" began to be used to describe an attempt to identify the characteristics of a perpetrator, such as a lone assassin or serial rapist.

- It was a small team of FBI analysts who first began to use the term "offender profiling" to describe how investigators could infer who an offender might be from the clues they leave while committing one or more crimes. A more formal term for this kind of analysis is "criminal personality profiling."

- Detectives have always used their past experience and their gut to try to identify criminals—and their motives—by looking at crime scenes, victims, and other clues.

- Criminal investigative analysis is crime analysis from a behavioral perspective. It's more scientific than what many think of as profiling because there's actual research behind it. Criminal investigative analysis ties both the investigator and a psychological researcher together to help understand violent crimes and solve specific cases.

- Criminal investigative analysis is used by the National Center for the Analysis of Violent Crime (NCAVC), which works on unsolved cases involving terrorism, threatened use of weapons of mass destruction, homicides, rapes, arsons, bombings, workplace and school violence, extortion, kidnapping, and missing persons. In these cases, NCAVC uses criminal investigative analysis in 3 main areas: the development of suspects, the interview and interrogation of potential suspects, and the clearing of innocent persons from suspicion.

Profiling a Perpetrator

- When these types of behavioral theories are applied with the goal of identifying a suspect, the investigators are really looking to determine the offender's motivation, his or her criminal sophistication, and whether he or she had a prior relationship with the victim of the crime. To do this, they can study the victims, survey the crime scene, and consider any physical objects or property that was taken during the commission of a crime.

- To profile the perpetrator, analysts may first consider the victim: Was the victim at a high, moderate, or low risk for this type of crime? Analysts must not make value judgments on the victims; instead, they

Investigators who perform profiling are behavioral scientists or behavioral analysts but use an interdisciplinary approach.

should be looking for the type of predator that would view the victim as a target and why. Behavioral analysts may also consider the victim's personality to help develop a suspect.

- There are typically 3 reasons that a perpetrator would take something away from a victim or away from a crime scene: the item has evidentiary value, such as a ski mask worn during a rape; the item has monetary value, such as a victim's watch or jewelry; or the item is seen as a souvenir for what is viewed as an accomplishment or victory.

- Criminal investigative analysis will also take into account evidence left at the crime scene from a behavioral standpoint. Essentially, investigators are looking for things that don't fit the typical scenario to see if they could have meaning and give insight into the killer or the killer's motive.

- With regard to homicides, behavioral analysis breaks down offenders into 2 main categories: organized and disorganized. For example, Ted Bundy was organized. His crimes were planned and rehearsed: They took into account the victims and their locations, what tools he would need to carry out the crime, and what things he needed to take from the scene in order to minimize being identified and apprehended.

- Disorganized killers are impulsive; they do not plan their attack, and they use whatever tools are available at the crime scene. Disorganized killers typically leave much more evidence behind, but they might become more organized if they are not caught early in their career.

- There are other related behavioral clues that analysts use when looking at homicide crime scenes. For example, was the body moved to another location or left where the victim fell? Did the perpetrator leave the body where the victim would be found in a reasonably short amount of time or in such a way that the body may not be found for a long time—if ever?

- Sometimes at homicide scenes, the body might be physically posed. Investigators might look for behavioral clues, such as whether the body was posed to offend the person who discovers the victim, to offend society in general, or to express the perpetrator's inner thoughts toward the victim or toward whom the victim represents.

Linking Crimes by Profiling

- Analyzing violent crime scenes from a profiling perspective can also include a determination of how the victim was approached or controlled by focusing on the clues from the scene that relate to understanding how the perpetrator works in terms of victim selection.

- Serial killer Ted Bundy had an idealized standard for his victims—and it wasn't just that they were attractive and typically had long brown hair that was parted down the middle. He had a behavioral standard that he tested when he approached them, and they had to be worthy of selection, in his mind. In a very real and creepy sense, Bundy actually profiled his own victims.

- Traditionally, serial offenses have been linked by modus operandi (M.O.), which is the method of operation. When perpetrators have a particular M.O., it's a pattern that typically helps enable them to successfully complete their criminal act in some way—either physically or psychologically—helps prevent their identification, and/or eases their escape from the location of the crime. The problem is that modus operandi can change over time.

- Another telling link between crimes is what's known as a perpetrator's signature. A criminal signature is not something that's necessary to accomplish any particular purpose; instead, a signature is based on some type of inner or psychological drive that comes from the offender's fantasies.

- Using all the behavioral clues gathered from the victim, crime scene, modus operandi, and any particular signature, investigators can attempt to hone in on the perpetrator. Although the ultimate goal is to identify the perpetrator, criminal personality profiling narrows down the field of all potential suspects to a more select pool of suggested individuals.

- Criminal personality profiling can also lead to an understanding of a perpetrator's fantasies, which can be positive or negative.

The offender's fantasies may be vague, repeated thoughts or very detailed, elaborately thought-out plans. These fantasies will often relate to the signature that is left behind.

- Investigators can also surmise clues as to a perpetrator's personality by things like whether he shows concern for personal risk—for example, did the offender take into account the time of day, the potential for witnesses, did he show the need to conceal his identity, did he appear to be wary of alarms or security cameras.

- The goal is to create a profile that can be released to the public that sufficiently describes the offender in a way that his or her own associates will recognize the offender and bring their suspicions to the authorities.

- Depending on the amount of information authorities have, a criminal profile may include the suspect's sex, race, approximate age, education level, criminal history, employment history, living location, social adjustment, and interpersonal skills.

- Once the profile is developed, authorities will create a strategy for a series of media releases and typically sequence them in such a way that they present the most confident information first to see where it leads the public or what effect it has on the perpetrator before adding and releasing additional detail.

Unsuccessful Profiling

- Over a 3-week period in October 2002 in the Washington DC area, 10 people were shot and killed and 3 others were badly wounded in sniper-style attacks while doing simple, everyday tasks.

- Because of the proximity to the I-95 corridor, it was suspected that the shooter was traveling that stretch of highway, and somehow, suspicion centered on a white van as the likely vehicle involved. The general conclusion was that the sniper was a loner—a white male who had a background in the military.

- It seemed that every conclusion that was released by the media caused the shooter to defy it. The media reported that the sniper only killed adults, and then a 13-year-old boy was shot; the media indicated that the shooter only attacked during the week, so he attacked on a weekend.

- In reality, these horrible killings were perpetrated by a black male and his young black accomplice from their specially designed trunk in a blue Chevrolet sedan. The pair later admitted to changing their victims and M.O. based on what they heard in the media.

- Profilers learned a grave lesson from this incident: You can get tunnel vision when you focus solely on past tendencies in crime and crime statistics and generate a profile that's one size fits all. It's especially dangerous to allow the investigation to eliminate, or at least narrow the pool of suspects, with so few details.

Successful Profiling

- Over a nearly 20-year period beginning in 1978, American terrorist Ted Kaczynski meticulously planned and carried out 16 bombings across the United States. He used homemade devices that became increasingly sophisticated over the years and were sent by mail or, in some cases, delivered by hand.

- Because Kaczynski's targets included universities and airlines, the FBI called him the Unabomber: "Un" for university and "a" for airline. Kaczynski was a Harvard graduate and then became a mathematics professor at University of California, Berkeley, but he ultimately became a recluse with a grudge against the world.

- Essentially, the motive for Kaczynski's crimes was his notion that big corporations and modern technology were destroying personal freedom. His attacks killed 3 people and injured 23 others—not one of whom ever saw his face.

- John Douglas, who has been called the FBI's mind hunter, was one of the Bureau's first criminal profilers. In 1980, he produced a criminal personality profile of the Unabomber, describing him as a white male in his late 20s to early 30s who was an obsessive-compulsive loner with connections to academia and who was of above-average intelligence.

- Eventually, in April of 1995, the Unabomber began communicating with the media. Kaczynski's communications and threats escalated, culminating in a 35,000-word manifesto that he wanted published in *The New York Times* and *The Washington Post*. The manifesto verified everything that Douglas had believed about the Unabomber and his motives.

- This time, the media worked to the profiler's advantage: After the Unabomber's manifesto was printed by the press in September of 1994, Kaczynski's brother came forward to tell authorities what his worst fears had been telling him: The Unabomber was his brother.

Suggested Reading

Alison, *Forensic Psychologist's Casebook.*

DeNevi, Campbell, Band, and Otto, *Into the Minds of Madmen.*

Douglas and Olshaker, *The Anatomy of Motive.*

Esherick, *Criminal Psychology and Personality Profiling.*

Napier, *Behavior, Truth, and Deception.*

Zulawski, Wicklander, Sturman, and Hoover, *Practical Aspects of Interview and Interrogation.*

Questions to Consider

1. What does the term "profiling" mean in a forensic context?

2. How and when is criminal profiling used?

3. What is meant by the term "victimology"?

Human Memory and Eyewitness Accounts
Lecture 28

Many people around the world have been convicted of crimes, including very serious ones, on evidence that doesn't rise to scientific standards, and one innocent person suffering is one too many. Today's technology—specifically, DNA testing—has definitively proven that people have been convicted of crimes they did not commit and, in some cases, after they've been executed for those crimes. Among the reasons that erroneous guilty verdicts occur is faulty eyewitness testimony, and among the reasons that eyewitness testimony is unreliable is the way human memory works—or doesn't.

Human Memory

- Memory is not a video recorder, where everything is seen in the mind's eye objectively and exactly as it happened. A memory is more of an impression of an event—including input from all of our senses—with some things noted correctly but others possibly changed a bit by pulling in elements from other events that may have created the same type of impression in our minds.

- Depending on our past experiences, our brains put different things we've experienced into different categories, or schema, for future recall. When an event occurs that fits one of our schema, our brain pulls out all of the bits of that schema to process the new information, and the overlap can mix things up a bit.

- Although there are different classification schemes, some researchers have categorized 4 types of memories: cognitive, motor-vestibular, emotional or affective, and state.

  o Cognitive memories are things our brain processes based on sequences and patterns—for example, learning names, phone numbers, and language.

- o Motor-vestibular memories are processed by our brain based on input from the body as a whole—for example, remembering how to ride a bike even though you haven't done it in years.

- o Emotional, sometimes called affective, memories are things our brain handles based on input from our gut emotions—such as grief, fear, and anger.

- o State memories are those our brain processes based on our senses. Because state memories can encompass input from all of our senses, they seem to be the most helpful in developing eyewitness accounts.

- There are also 2 stages of memory: Short-term memory involves the information that our brain doesn't process for future recall because it's seen as unimportant data while long-term, or permanent, memory is deemed important and, therefore, is stored and can be retrieved.

Auditory memories of what people think they hear during a crime are even less reliable than what people think they see.

- Most researchers believe information has to be processed in short-term memory before being stored in long-term memory, but others think that the information can go directly to long-term storage while an experience is happening.

- Whether or not we remember an event or person depends on how our brain dealt with the relevant information at the time of the event or encounter, and there are many variables that affect this processing, many of which have been discovered and verified by scientific research.

Problems with Forensic Eyewitness Testimony
- Eyewitness testimony is problematic for many reasons that are related to the unreliability of our human information-processing system. Details get mixed up over time, and how and what we commit to memory and are able to recall is selective.

- In addition, our memories are influenced by our beliefs, motives, stress, stereotypes, and various environmental factors. There are many reasons that no 2 people come away from the exact same experience with the same memory of it.

- In relation to forensic eyewitness testimony and perpetrator identification, psychologists have identified 2 main groups of influences: estimation factors and system variables. Estimation factors are things about memory and recall that are related to the victim, perpetrator, and crime while system variables are influences on memory and recall that come from police and legal procedures.

- A common estimation factor is cross-racial identification bias: For some reason, human brains are wired to more clearly identify individuals who are of the same race as they are. This isn't the same as being racist; it's an inability of human brains to identify distinctions between faces of other races.

- In addition, studies have shown that some faces are simply easier to remember, recognize, and describe than others. Faces that are more distinct—such as people who are considered particularly attractive or especially unattractive—tend to be better remembered than those that are considered typical or average.

- There are also inherent differences between witnesses. Children and elderly witnesses tend to remember things less correctly than young or middle-aged adults. Their descriptors may mean different things as well—for example, to a 6-year-old child, "really old" could mean someone who was 30.

- People employed in a certain profession may remember details related to that profession. Research also suggests that men tend to pay attention to different details than women do; the brains of men and women seem to be wired differently in certain ways.

- Some people are just better with faces than others, and even if someone is good at recognizing or remembering faces, sometimes they still can't figure out how to describe that face to someone else.

- Studies suggest that someone who is a crime victim may even inadvertently change the face of the perpetrator as a subconscious defense mechanism. This seems to happen especially in cases of a sexual assault, where the victim's brain actually tries to make the perpetrator's face more attractive to better cope with the mental trauma.

- The level of involvement and awareness as a crime takes places also plays a role in how much attention is paid to the events and, therefore, how well things are remembered. A victim or bystander who realizes a crime is being committed will be paying more attention as events unfold than a witness who doesn't even know what's happening until it's over.

- If there was drug or alcohol use on the part of the victim or another witness—or if either has a cognitive disability—the way something is remembered may not be accurate. Even if the person is very certain about how things happened, the testimony may not work well in court because it could always be called into question by the defense.

- Stress also plays a huge part in misidentification. In the weapon-focus effect, if a weapon is present in a situation, the witness will tend to focus on the weapon more than the suspect, which can cause incorrect or inadequate memory of the perpetrator and other parts of the event.

- The setting also plays a role in how much someone remembers. For example, a suspect seen in full daylight is more likely to be recalled with accuracy than if the same person was walking down a dark street.

- The length of time between an incident and when it's recalled also has an effect on the way things are remembered. In fact, it's been shown that in as little as 20 minutes, people can have a sharp decrease in the number of correct things they remember about a particular event.

Minimizing Bias in System Variables

- When a witness is being interviewed, the way questions are worded or comments are made can affect how something is remembered by the witness. For example, a question such as "Did he have a gun?" can cause an individual to remember a gun—even if one wasn't actually present during the crime. Instead, use open-ended or possibly multiple-choice questions.

- Two things you don't see on television is that pausing before asking another question may give the witness enough time to find another detail in their memory and that a person should always be told that they can say, "I don't know" if they don't recall something so that they don't try to fill in gaps with details that aren't true.

- Sometimes, it's also helpful—depending on the emotional state of the victim or witness—to have the witness physically walk through the scene and describe how events unfolded. There may be details that were seen at the time that were filed in long-term memory that don't come to the surface until the events are replayed.

- Some of the problems with police lineups—when a string of possible suspects is paraded before a witness—include witnesses being pressured by officers, who maybe tell the witness that their testimony is the only evidence that the police have.

- The current best practice for conducting a lineup is to have a double-blind scenario. In this situation, the officers interacting with the witness during a lineup don't even know which person is the suspect. This double-blind setup helps to eliminate experimenter bias, which involves the officer leading the witness to choose a certain suspect from the lineup—either intentionally or unconsciously.

- When conducting a lineup, the officer should tell the witness that the perpetrator may or may not be in the lineup so that the witness doesn't feel like he or she has to make an identification from those shown, which might cause the witness to choose the person who most closely resembles the criminal. As a test, authorities can also do a culprit-absent lineup, where the criminal is not actually in the lineup.

- It's also recommended that the members of a lineup be presented sequentially—one after the other and one at a time—to try to minimize the effects of relative judgment by not allowing the witness to look back and forth between possible suspects to determine which most closely fits the picture of the perpetrator in their mind.

- In addition, it's recommended that everyone in a lineup or photo array be an innocent "filler" person except the suspect and that these other people fairly closely resemble the original description of the suspect. If the witness picks one of the "fillers" instead of the actual suspect, law enforcement will know that the witness's recall may be questionable.

- There have been cases where a witness wasn't 100% sure they picked the right person at a police lineup, but during preparation for trial or under direct or cross-examination at trial, the wording of questions posed by lawyers make the witness more confident about the identification. However, witnesses who seemed credible up to that point have also become uncertain when questioned again. In situations like these, it's imperative that there be other evidence besides a witness to convict or exonerate a suspect.

- There are also instances where a supposed witness knowingly and deliberately misidentifies someone. This may be to get attention and sympathy or to direct suspicion away from themselves.

- It's been suggested that in cases where a suspect is fabricated, there are often some telltale signs. These make-believe suspects tend to commit their fabricated crimes in copycat fashion after a similar crime gets publicized in the media. Police also look for damage or injuries that are inconsistent with the story given by the self-proclaimed victim.

- Currently, the federal standard for eyewitness testimony in court is that if a witness is very sure of his or her testimony, it is admissible in court. If there's an amount of uncertainty, it's up to the judge in the particular case to decide whether to allow it or not. However, studies have shown that the degree of certainty of a witness doesn't necessarily correlate with the reliability of his or her testimony.

Suggested Reading

Eisen, Quas, and Goodman, *Memory and Suggestibility in the Forensic Interview*.

Loftus, *Eyewitness Testimony*.

Tapper, "Criminal Law Revision Committee 11th Report."

Zulawski, Wicklander, Sturman, and Hoover, *Practical Aspects of Interview and Interrogation*.

1. How reliable is memory?

2. What kinds of things affect a person's memory of an event, particularly involving criminal activity?

3. Is eyewitness testimony direct or circumstantial evidence?

Criminal Minds—Psychology and Psychiatry
Lecture 29

T he study of human behavior is essentially what psychology is, and the entire legal system is really all about managing human behavior. Motive and the behavior it causes create crime scenes, evidence, and victims—both dead and living—which, in turn, set law enforcement into action. Forensic psychology and forensic psychiatry are the 2 formal disciplines that work together to apply psychological and pertinent medical findings to legal processes. There are clear overlaps between the uses of psychology and psychiatry in forensic science and also some distinctions between the 2 fields.

Roles and Responsibilities of Forensic Psychologists and Psychiatrists

- Over the course of the 20th century, mental health practitioners—mostly psychiatrists in the early days—began evaluating and even treating criminal defendants in the United States. The bulk of the psychology mostly involved pretrial examinations to look at issues of competency and responsibility, and some of the work was intended to help judges determine how to sentence convicted offenders, especially those involved in sex crimes.

- The roles and responsibilities of forensic psychologists and psychiatrists can essentially be divided up into 3 areas: assessment, treatment, and testimony.

    o Assessment involves evaluating people under the supervision of the legal system using a variety of psychological tests.

    o Treatment can involve psychotherapy, behavioral modification exercises, and other mental health therapy options. Treatment medications can be prescribed by forensic psychiatrists, who are medical doctors.

o   Forensic psychologists and psychiatrists may be asked to provide testimony as experts on human behavior and mental health issues.

- Psychologists and psychiatrists work in both civil and criminal areas of the legal system. Civil law issues include family matters of custody and juvenile delinquency as well as legal concerns of a noncriminal nature. However, criminal forensic psychology and psychiatry issues include competency to stand trial, legal insanity, sentencing matters, and treatment of mentally ill offenders.

Psychologists versus Lawyers

- Lawyers have the job of trying to establish who is guilty of a crime or responsible for an accident; their job is to establish fault. However, psychologists are taught not to make moral judgments but, rather, try to understand why a patient or client did what he or she did.

- The legal system is always on a calendar or time clock. Psychologists tend to work to understand what happened or what is happening, regardless of how long it takes for them and their patient to get there.

- Lawyers need definite answers to close a case whereas psychologists deal more with theories than answers. There are many cases where the world will never know why a person did what he or she did or understand the pathology behind his or her motivation.

- It is part of a lawyer's job to put a spin on the testimony or evidence in the case or attempt to choose only what parts of that information get presented in court, but an objective forensic psychologist should be more interested in telling the whole story.

Forensic Psychology versus Clinical Psychology

- Forensic psychologists and psychiatrists usually have a pretty narrowly defined area of assessment about a specific event or pattern of events in a client's past and a specific diagnosis or treatment plan is not the primary goal. In clinical psychology, however, the practitioner is really focused on the patient's problems and treatment needs.

- The focus in clinical psychology is often on the patient's view of a situation while a forensic psychologist needs to get a picture of the entire situation—not just the client's perspective.

- A huge difference between clinical and forensic psychology is that patients generally go voluntarily to see a clinical psychologist, but assessments by a forensic psychologist are done as a result of a court order or an attorney's recommendation.

- Clinical psychologists and their patients can decide together what they want to do—or not do—while in the office, but in forensic psychological settings, there are legal statutes that govern the interaction.

- Patients of a clinical psychologist—if they're not interested in wasting their time and money—will generally tell the truth because they want to improve their life or mental state. On the other hand, in a forensic psychology setting, suspects or criminals may purposefully distort the truth to either make themselves look better or to help their case.

- Interactions between a clinical psychologist and a patient emphasize caring, trust, and empathy, and most issues are to be kept confidential. However, forensic mental health examiners may not be seen by patients as being there to help them, and forensic psychologists can't become sympathetic to the defendant because that could limit their objectivity. There are also limits on the amount of information that's considered confidential in forensic psychology, especially since criminal activity is involved.

Evaluating and Assessing Mental Health
- Researchers have developed many standardized analytical tests to try to get quantitative or otherwise objective results

that may help the authorities understand a person who is being assessed.

Mental health experts, such as psychologists and psychiatrists, both aid and inform the legal system.

- General personality inventories, such as the Myers-Briggs test, and projective personality tests, such as the famous Rorschach test, are used in all areas of psychology. Other tests are used to gauge a person's general intellectual capacity, memory function, and neuropsychological impairments or specific disorders.

- A host of specialized forensic psychological assessment tests have been developed for use in legal settings. Some relate to the comprehension of Miranda and other legal rights during interrogation, and others gauge a person's competence to stand trial. A test called the Rogers Criminal Responsibility Assessment Scales can be used to evaluate legal insanity.

- There are also some forensic assessment tests that relate more specifically to civil law, such as the Ackerman-Schoendorf Scales for parent evaluation that is used in child custody and related issues. Other tests help determine someone's competence within the community, such as whether they need a guardian. The Hopkins Competency Assessment Test can be used to help gauge a person's capacity for decision making regarding medical treatment.

- Both psychologists and psychiatrists can use these types of evaluative tools to try to measure a person's mental health, personality, intelligence, and risk to others in society. In addition, because they are physicians, psychiatrists can add physical exams, lab tests, and different types of brain studies and other diagnostic tools not open to psychologists.

- When psychologists and psychiatrists give expert testimony in court, they are not there to officially answer legal questions, such as whether or not an individual is or was insane—that's up to the judge or jury. Forensic psychologists and psychiatrists are simply called upon to give their best judgment about a person in a legal setting.

Deception by Defendants

- Psychologists break types of deception into different categories. One of them is known as malingering, which is sometimes called simulation. This is when a defendant is consciously pretending to have a mental illness, perhaps to try to avoid being prosecuted by showing that he or she could not be guilty by reason of insanity.

- Interestingly, when defendants are trying to fake symptoms of a mental illness, they'll usually pick one that's getting a lot of attention in the media at the time. The same is true for multiple personality disorder, also known as dissociative identity disorder, which has been heavily popularized in books and Hollywood productions.

- One of the ways that forensic psychologists and psychiatrists recognize the difference between people who truly have a psychiatric disorder and those who are malingering is that fake symptoms are almost always over the top. However, it's difficult to maintain the symptoms of a disease you don't have for very long, and these types of deceptions are usually pretty quickly uncovered.

- The opposite type of deception is known as defensiveness, sometimes called dissimulation, which is when the defendant—or someone who's already been convicted—consciously professes not to have a mental illness when in fact he or she does. People sometimes try this in order to get released from prison or a mental facility, if that's where they're being housed.

- In cases known as pseudomalingering, a mentally ill person will pretend to have the mental illness they actually do have, often to try to give them a feeling of control. Some defendants claim—and may actually believe—a different motive than what their actual intention was.

- Then, there are deceptive people, including criminal defendants, who are just plain lying. Obviously, this can be simply to avoid responsibility for their actions and the penalty that comes with it, but it may also be to enhance their own mental image of who they are or to have a feeling of superiority over others by smugly thinking that everyone else is too stupid to realize that they're lying.

- In criminal settings, forensic psychologists and forensic psychiatrists may be called on to distinguish between truth, deception, and mental illness. Their judgments are based on behavioral science research and the assessment tests and other diagnostic tools at their disposal.

Competency as a Mental State

- In both civil and criminal matters, specifically related to the courtroom setting, people can be examined by psychologists and psychiatrists to see if they are competent to testify or competent to waive legal representation.

- In essence, with regard to the criminal justice system, people are evaluated to make sure they can understand and participate rationally in what goes on in the courtroom, including what may go on afterward.

- In criminal cases, defendants may even be examined to see if they are competent to be executed—to make sure they understand the finality of what that means and why they could receive the death penalty in a courtroom proceeding.

- There are 3 types of competency that are related to criminal forensic psychology and psychiatry: competent in the present, competent in the past, and competent in the future.

  o Competency in the present addresses whether the person is capable enough to give a statement to the police, to stand trial, or to testify. This is usually done in the pretrial or trial phases of a case. If someone is found incompetent to stand trial, they are usually hospitalized for treatment, and if they get better, a trial might actually take place.

  o Competent in the past has to do with legal insanity and is typically part of the trial phase in a case. Most jurisdictions follow the McNaughten rule, which basically states that if the defendant did not or could not understand what he or she was doing—or that it was wrong—at the time of the crime, they are considered "not guilty by reason of insanity."

  o Competency in the future is really a prediction of a person's dangerousness and is usually part of the posttrial phase in a case. This is very tricky because psychologists and psychiatrists have to base future possibilities on past performance.

- Jeffrey Dahmer, who killed at least 17 men over a period of 13 years in the 1970s and 1980s, originally pled not guilty by reason of insanity, but the goal-oriented nature of his crimes and his lack of delusions and other psychoses seemed to negate that plea, and he ultimately changed it to guilty but insane. Dahmer was found sane and guilty on 15 counts of murder, and the judge sentenced him to nearly 1000 years in prison, which was 15 life terms.

Suggested Reading

Alison, *Forensic Psychologist's Casebook.*

Douglas and Olshaker, *The Anatomy of Motive.*

Eisen, Quas, and Goodman, *Memory and Suggestibility in the Forensic Interview.*

Esherick, *Criminal Psychology and Personality Profiling.*

Ewing, *Minds on Trial.*

Huss, *Forensic Psychology.*

Rogers, *Clinical Assessment of Malingering and Deception.*

Tapper, "Criminal Law Revision Committee 11th Report."

Questions to Consider

1. What is the difference between forensic psychology and forensic psychiatry?

2. How are the behavioral sciences used in forensics?

3. What do you know about different types of deception in regard to forensic science?

4. What does it mean for a person to be "competent" in a legal sense?

When Forensic Evidence Is on Trial
Lecture 30

What sets forensic science apart from other scientific endeavors is that the results of forensic analyses may end up in the courtroom. Forensic evidence of any type—whether a physical artifact or what someone has to say—must be collected, prepared, and analyzed with the mindset that it may end up in court someday. That's the reason behind the chain of custody for physical evidence and why interviews have to be carried out within legal constraints.

Criminal Cases versus Civil Issues

- Criminal cases are those where a person allegedly did something that's an offense to all of society. There might be a specific victim that a person robbed, raped, or otherwise harmed, but that person's actions broke the rules we've created to manage human behavior.

- As part of his or her journey to the courtroom, a person that commits a crime is first indicted for the crime by the grand jury, which formally accuses the person by the legal system. Then, some governmental entity will prosecute the case—such as the U.S. Attorney General's Office, if a federal law was broken, or the state in which the crime occurred, if a state law was broken.

- The government party is called the plaintiff, and the person that committed the crime is the defendant. The victim doesn't have to bring the case to the court—and, in some cases, may not even be alive to do so. Some crimes don't really have a victim, such as speeding or driving while intoxicated.

- In criminal cases, there may not be a trial because the person may plead out at a pretrial hearing. However, if the person is found guilty at the end of a trial, he or she will be sentenced, which might involve paying a fine or restitution to the victim, being on probation, or going to jail or prison.

- On the other hand, civil cases are about disagreements between people and/or institutions—such as businesses or the government. To start a civil case, a person or some representative of an organization makes a claim against another person or institution.

- Whoever makes that claim is the plaintiff, and whoever they allege harmed them—or failed to fulfill an obligation to them—is called the defendant.

- In some cases, people can bring a civil suit against a government entity for what they perceive as a violation of their rights; likewise, the government can bring a civil suit against a corporation for violating a legal statute, for example.

- After a civil case is heard, a decision is made regarding who is responsible or who owes what to the other party. If what's owed is financial, the penalty costs are called damages. A person can't be sent to jail from a civil case.

Forensic Evidence and the Law

- Whether a civil or criminal matter, if forensic evidence is used, it's employed in the same way: to help the judge or jury reach a decision in the case. Either a judge or jury can be what are called the triers of a case in different types of trials. A bench trial is when the case is heard before one or more judges only. A jury trial has a judge but also a group of 6 to 12 jurors, plus alternates who can fill in if necessary, selected to hear the case.

- It's always the judge that determines admissibility of evidence in any case, and it's the triers of fact, whether judge or jury, that reach a decision of guilt or innocence—or fault, in the case of a civil trial—by applying the relevant law to the admissible evidence and facts established in the case. The jury may play a role in setting punishment, but it's usually up to the judge. This sentencing may even involve another hearing in the penalty phase of the trial.

- It's the job of the attorneys to present evidence to support the side of the case they represent. There are prosecuting and defense attorneys in criminal cases and attorneys for the plaintiff and defendant in civil cases. Legal jurisdictions have prosecutors that they employ, and the defendant can either hire an attorney or be represented by a public defender, who is assigned to present their evidence.

- Evidence can be tangible items—or reports about them—photos, documents, drugs, bullets, and fingerprints. Evidence also consists of eyewitness testimony, law enforcement testimony, and expert testimony. Some evidence that is gathered in a forensic case ends up in court, and other times it doesn't, so all evidence must be treated as if it will be presented in court someday.

- In reality, most of the work that forensic scientists and police officers do is not presented or testified to in court. There's always the possibility that what they discover is that no crime was committed, or that their work exonerates someone, so no charges are ever brought.

- Even if a defendant is charged or a civil case is initiated, the defendant may simply plead guilty—which happens all the time, especially when they are shown the mounting evidence against them—or there may be a plea bargain to a lesser charge. In these types of cases, any lesser charges might render some forensic evidence unnecessary in court. In some cases, when the trial seems to be going in a particular direction—or possibly nowhere—the charges can be dropped, so evidence or testimony isn't needed.

Trial Preparation

- Part of trial preparation is collecting information from witnesses and getting evidence ready. This may include issuing subpoenas that compel people to come to court or taking pretrial depositions. A deposition is when one or more attorneys question a potential witness, under oath, but outside the courtroom. Sometimes, forensic reports will be used to substitute for court appearances by forensic scientists, so attorneys may gather and review reports.

- Discovery has to do with the sharing of information between parties involved in litigation. There's been a shift to broaden discovery in criminal cases in the United States because in the past, the defendant was not entitled to see the prosecution's evidence. Each side of the case prepares a discovery motion for the judge, asking to see documents like witness lists and forensic reports so that they know what type of evidence may be coming.

The legal system sets forth rules that govern evidence and testimony about evidence.

- In some jurisdictions, there's an exception to discovery in murder cases. The prosecution doesn't have to divulge the names of key witnesses until the morning each is to take the stand so that they can't be tampered with, threatened, or killed before testifying.

- Physical evidence needs to be prepared for court and is called demonstrative evidence when a scientist is going to use it to demonstrate his or her findings. Sometimes, the actual evidence is used in court, but usually, enlarged photographs are used because a lot of evidence is either tiny or transient.

- Reconstruction evidence may include computer animations—such as an accident reconstruction—or even physical demonstrations, such as an officer standing up and showing the jury exactly how he or she put the suspect in a choke hold.

- With regard to physical evidence, photographs, and lab reports, once the judge admits an item into evidence, the court reporter will continue the chain of custody by maintaining an accurate record and securing all evidence in a court lockup area for the duration of the trial. Later, if there's an appeal, the tangible items can be signed out, and transcripts of the testimony can be gathered.

Evidence Standards

- Evidence is divided into 2 main categories: circumstantial and direct evidence.

- Circumstantial evidence includes blood, hair, fibers, fingerprints, and even DNA. Despite the fact that some physical evidence can be directly tied to a single individual, it alone doesn't prove who committed the crime; it only shows that the evidence was at the scene, assuming a good chain of custody. Circumstantial evidence requires that an inference be made about it.

- Direct evidence is eyewitness testimony, which is notoriously unreliable. Direct evidence supports an assertion without the need for any inference. It's up to the judge or jury—as triers of fact—to evaluate all evidence, including the testimony of eyewitnesses or experts.

- There are many rules that govern evidence—whether physical items or testimony. Any court ruling is subject to challenge, and that's why matters are often taken to a higher court for what's called an appeal. In an appeal, what is challenged in a trial can be further ruled upon, and decisions can be either upheld or overturned.

- The 2 standards that all evidence—scientific or otherwise—must meet in order to be admissible in court are relevance and competence.

- For evidence to be relevant, it has to be both material and probative. Material means that the evidence has to pertain to the matter at hand; it can't be evidence from a previous incident. Probative means that the evidence has to relate to proving something in the case; it has to make something either more likely or less likely than it would be without the support of that evidence.

- To be admissible, evidence also has to have competence. To be competent, evidence has to be free of prejudice, must meet all constitutional constraints, has to be allowable under the privileges set out by law, and can't be hearsay.

The Admissibility of Scientific Evidence

- The general rules of evidence—relevance and competency—still hold with scientific evidence, but additional rules have emerged because of how complicated technical and scientific evidence might be to a nonexpert.

- An interesting legal case involving James Frye in the early 1920s was the impetus behind our current standards for scientific evidence. The Frye decision evolved into general acceptance, which means that novel or experimental scientific techniques are not admissible in court; only methods that are generally accepted by the scientific community can be admitted into evidence. While hard to define, general acceptance more or less came to mean that the science was published in a peer-reviewed journal.

- Article VII, Rule 702 of the Federal Rules of Evidence, which was created in the 1970s, specifically addresses expert testimony—including that of scientists—and requires that expert witnesses demonstrate their qualifications in court and show that their opinions would aid the triers of fact in a case.

- In 1993, another case heavily influenced the admissibility of scientific evidence: *Daubert v. Merrell Dow*. The Daubert standard holds that valid science has to meet the following criteria, which enhance and expand on general acceptance.

    o Valid science needs to hold up to scientific testing designed to show any falsifiability.

    o It must use the appropriate standards and scientific controls to assure its accuracy.

o   Admissible science needs to present statistics on its known error rates—though they may need to be explained to the jury.

o   Worthy science must stand up to peer review and publication within the scientific community.

- A 2009 report by the National Academy of Science (NAS) recommended that a federal agency be created to oversee and fund research, training, and the development of standards in forensics as well as regulations that will govern all crime labs. The NAS report is changing, and will continue to change, the way forensic science works.

Suggested Reading

Ewing, *Minds on Trial*.

Feder and Houck, *Feder's Succeeding as an Expert Witness*.

Shelton, *Forensic Science in Court*.

Questions to Consider

1.   What is the difference between a criminal trial and a civil trial?

2.   What is the difference between a jury trial and a bench trial?

3.   How is evidence prepared for trial?

4.   What types of things make evidence admissible in the courtroom?

5.   How does the admissibility of scientific evidence differ from the admissibility of other types of evidence?

Forensic Scientists and Expert Testimony
Lecture 31

I n the courtroom, an expert witness and his or her testimony vary greatly from that of an eyewitness. An expert can be any person who—through their training, education, experience, published works, membership in professional organizations, or some combination of those—could assist a judge or jury by giving an opinion on a disputed matter. Most importantly, expert witnesses are bound by common ethical principles to work only for the truth—anything more or less than that is unacceptable.

The Importance of Expert Testimony

- Materiality and relevance pertain to an expert witness just as they would any other type of evidence, so attorneys have to make sure that the expert witness they plan to call to the stand has something potentially important to say about the matter in question. They also need to research the expert's qualifications, which need to satisfy the triers of fact that the person giving expert testimony really is a bona fide expert on the subject.

- Qualifying a witness to serve as an expert can be a lengthy process of questioning the potential witness on his or her background, or it can be simply stipulated to by the attorneys on both sides of the case.

- When you see multiple experts being asked about their backgrounds in courtrooms on television, that's not necessarily far from the way it happens in real life. The prosecution gets to call their experts, and the defense gets to do likewise. That's because in any kind of legal dispute, both sides have the right to good science.

- Part of being an expert witness is that he or she is not there to win or lose a case in the way an attorney might be. An expert witness is there to help the jury or the judge understand things that aren't familiar to most people. Unfortunately, there are some forensic scientists who have the reputation among their colleagues as being people who will say just about anything to make money.

Assisting the Triers of Fact

- Ordinary witnesses can really only give courtroom testimony that comes from the personal knowledge they've gained by using their eyes and ears—which can't always be trusted. Ordinary witnesses aren't allowed to give opinions about the things they saw or heard; they can only report them.

- However, forensic scientists and other expert witnesses can testify not only about personal knowledge gained from their eyes and ears, but can also form opinions based on their evaluation of evidence through scientific testing.

- To be good expert witnesses, forensic scientists have to be able to explain complex scientific topics in a way that any person chosen to sit on a jury could understand.

- A good attorney directs the questioning in such a way as to ensure that the expert witness's answers give the jury what they need to know. Even though it can be uncomfortable, the attorneys need to make the appropriate legal objections if the witness strays into areas that could be damaging to their case.

- In the courtroom, the attorneys and the judge carefully control the order and amount of information released because they are the experts charged with making sure testimony meets the appropriate legal standards.

- Because our legal system is adversarial—as it is portrayed in television or movie courtroom dramas—the attorneys also try to push for or limit information in a way that will support their side of the story. Unfortunately, expert witnesses don't have the right to refuse to answer a question just because it makes them or others feel uncomfortable.

Experts in Forensic Science

- Over the years, there has been a pretty big shift in forensic science that has been largely related to technology. Police officers used to be largely responsible for most of the standard forensic work that was done—not just investigation, but also recognizing, collecting, and preserving forensic evidence as well as analyzing it. Much of that work is still done today by law enforcement officers when it comes to areas such as fingerprints and motor-vehicle accidents.

- Unlike what you see on television, forensic scientists do not chase down leads, question suspects, or interview witnesses—except in specialized cases. The legwork that is conducted in the community, which is necessary to solve the case, is still done by law enforcement officers.

- As technology has advanced, some aspects of forensic science—especially related to analytical techniques—have become so dependent on an intense knowledge of chemistry, biology, and physics that much of the related lab work has become the domain of scientists.

- The first crime lab was established by Edmund Locard—of Locard's exchange principle—in 1910 in France, and the FBI forensic lab originated in 1932. However, it wasn't until 1937 that the first U.S. forensic science college program began at the University of California, Berkeley. Currently, there are well over 100 forensic science graduate programs in the United States alone—and that's just counting the programs beyond the 4-year bachelor's degree level.

- Because of the explosion of interest in forensic science that has been prompted largely by television shows, there's been a lot of pressure for colleges and universities to develop forensic science programs to recruit the interested public, but few of these programs are accredited by the Forensic Science Education Programs Accreditation Commission (FEPAC).

Career Pathways to Becoming a Forensic Expert

- The American Academy of Forensic Sciences, founded in 1948, is the premier professional organization for forensic scientists. It recognizes and encompasses 11 sections: criminalistics; digital and multimedia sciences; engineering sciences; jurisprudence; odontology; pathology and biology; physical anthropology; psychiatry and behavioral science; questioned documents; toxicology; and a general section, which is home to a variety of forensic specialists.

- Criminalists examine and test the broadest range of different types of physical evidence. They analyze hair, fibers, body fluids, chemicals, paint, glass, soil, flammable substances, firearms and bullets, toolmarks, and fingerprints.

- Typically, criminalists have a bachelor's degree in some type of physical or natural science, and many of them have master's degrees. Like all forensic scientists, criminalists have to engage in continuing education and may become certified by the American Board of Criminalistics.

© Hemera/Thinkstock.

Forensic entomologists, serologists, and DNA analysts are all forensic scientists who are members of the AAFS's pathology and biology section.

- Many different types of forensic settings employ criminalists in a full-time capacity, including sheriff and police departments, medical examiner's and coroner's offices, colleges and universities involved in forensic training, and state and federal agencies, such as the FBI and the CIA.

- The newest section in the American Academy of Forensic Sciences is the digital and multimedia sciences section. Experts in this field examine all types of digital devices and evidence—from computers and networks to cameras and cell phones.

- The educational background for these forensic experts is typically a bachelor's degree, usually in computer science, information technology, or engineering. There are career opportunities in large city and state law enforcement agencies as well as at the federal level, but unlike many other forensic science fields, digital specialists may also be employed in the private sector.

- Forensic engineers examine the causes of accidents, structural and manufacturing failures, and the origin of fires and explosions. Engineers primarily get involved in civil suits, such as personal injury or patent issues.

- They usually have an engineering degree that's followed by more specific training and experience in narrower aspects of engineering and possibly a graduate degree. Like some other forensic science specialties, forensic engineers usually have their own consulting business that's only partly devoted to forensic work.

- The jurisprudence section is made up of lawyers, including district and state attorneys, public defenders, judges, and college and university law professors. These professionals have a law degree, after which they pursue the continuing education necessary to support, refine, and advance the legal system—especially as it relates to forensic science.

- Experts in the field of forensic odontology begin with a Doctor of Dental Science (DDS) or Doctor of Dental Medicine (DMD) degree, but they need specific forensic training in order to be qualified as an expert in forensic dental identifications and bite-mark analysis.

- There are a few professional societies, institutes, and universities that offer additional training to forensic dentists, and the American Board of Forensic Odontology has a certification exam they can take. Most forensic odontologists do part-time forensic consulting aside from their full-time work in a regular dental practice.

- Experts who belong to the pathology and biology section are mostly forensic pathologists who are employed full time in coroner's and medical examiner's offices throughout North America. This means that they have gone to medical school, had a pathology residency, and then spent an additional 1 to 2 years in a forensic pathology fellowship program. The American Board of Pathology has an exam to certify expertise.

- Experts in physical anthropology usually hold a Ph.D. in anthropology or human biology with an emphasis on the human skeleton. There are practicing forensic anthropologists who hold master's degrees, but currently, the American Board of Forensic Anthropology will only allow those with doctoral degrees to sit for its certification exam, and applicants must have 3 years of experience beyond the Ph.D. before they take the exam.

- Most physical anthropologists have part-time forensic consulting practices in addition to full-time teaching responsibilities. There are a handful of full-time positions in forensic anthropology in larger medical examiner's and coroner's offices and some with the military and the FBI.

- Forensic experts in psychiatry and behavioral science have backgrounds related to their specific roles. Psychiatrists are medical doctors who pursue a residency in psychiatry and further education that is specific to forensic psychiatry. There is a certification exam through the American Board of Psychiatry and Neurology for forensic psychiatrists.

- Forensic psychologists have graduate training that typically includes a Ph.D. in psychology and postdoctoral work. They also may take a certification exam in forensic psychology through the American Board of Professional Psychology. Career opportunities in these areas include private practice as well as state and federal government positions in prisons, hospitals, and other settings.

- Unlike many of the other fields, questioned-document examiners have traditionally emerged out of law enforcement. In fact, there currently aren't any degree programs in the United States that specialize in forensic document examination.

- After a minimum of a bachelor's degree in science, criminalistics, or criminal justice, a person wanting to be a document examiner undertakes an apprenticeship or internship with an already established expert in the field. There is a certification exam through the American Board of Forensic Document Examiners, and professionals end up working in both public and private sectors.

- Experts in toxicology examine body substances to look for chemicals that may relate to cause of death or illness or chemicals that might impair a person's abilities or judgment. They also analyze questioned substances to determine their chemical makeup or to determine whether a product has been chemically tampered with.

- To be a toxicologist, a person needs a minimum of a bachelor's degree, usually in chemistry with an emphasis in pharmacology. Many professional toxicologists hold master's and doctoral degrees, and the American Board of Forensic Toxicology and the Forensic Toxicology Certification Board have professional certification exams. Most forensic toxicologists are employed full time in medical examiner's, coroner's, and law enforcement laboratories, but some also work in industry and government settings.

Suggested Reading

Ewing, *Minds on Trial*.

Feder and Houck, *Feder's Succeeding as an Expert Witness*.

Shelton, *Forensic Science in Court*.

Questions to Consider

1. What are the qualifications for an expert witness?

2. How is expert witness testimony different from the testimony of any other kind of witness?

3. What types of educational pathways lead to the various careers in forensic science?

Comparing Crimes and Crime Labs
Lecture 32

E ach forensic investigation starts off with a crime, or at least a suspected crime or suspicious death. Crime is everywhere—it's as old as humanity itself—but access to the tools to solve crimes is not everywhere. The forensic services available in different parts of the world—to process and analyze evidence and to help find criminals—vary tremendously around the world, just like other aspects of technology. The good news is that there are increasing trends toward worldwide cooperation in forensic science training.

Categorizing Crime

- There are several ways crime can be categorized. For example, there are major crimes and minor offenses, which don't cause as much harm to others or society. Some crimes are classified as felonies, which are more serious and carry heavier penalties than misdemeanor crimes.

- Advances in technology make it possible to commit crimes that pose new challenges to law enforcement, but many still employ a more traditional method of operations.

- There are 2 broad categories of crime: property crimes, those in which nobody's supposed to get hurt, and violent crimes, in which violence is intentional.

- Property crimes are those in which the target is nonhuman, such as arson, burglary, and motor-vehicle theft. Although people may be killed in the commission of those types of crimes, the initial intent of the perpetrators was to take something that didn't belong to them or to set something on fire—for various psychological reasons.

- Violent crimes are those in which the offenders set out to harm people or at least to threaten to harm them. Homicide, rape, aggravated assault, kidnapping, and robbery are examples of violent crimes.

- There's a key difference between burglary and robbery that makes burglary a property crime and robbery a violent crime. In a burglary, there's intentional unlawful entry into a building or somewhere else to steal things, but in a robbery, the property is stolen by violence or the threat of violence, and the criminal anticipates encountering a victim going into the act.

Studying Crime
- Crime is an area of significant study. Local, state, and federal agencies all collect data on different types of crimes and where and how often they occur.

- Each year, the FBI puts out their Uniform Crime Report called *Crime in the United States*, which breaks offenses into property crimes and violent crimes and then subdivides those categories further. They also give clearance rates on the percentage of reported crimes that have been resolved and, to some extent, by what means.

- Similar to the FBI report, since 1970, the United Nations has regularly conducted its Surveys on Crime Trends and the Operations of Criminal Justice Systems. The survey poses all types of questions to approximately 150 participating countries' governments, covering all types of information.

- The UN points out that reported crime in no way includes all crime. A large percentage of crime goes unreported to authorities, particularly lesser crimes, for a variety of reasons. There are also some inherent issues with making cross-country comparisons that the UN points out. Because definitions and reporting processes vary, data isn't always comparable. However, they do report their crime statistics per 100,000 people, which treats large and small countries equally.

- Another factor to consider in worldwide crime rates is that the more highly developed the society is, the more access people have to police stations, telephones, and even insurance—so crime is more likely to be reported. Also, in areas where governments are more corrupt, justice is less assured, and cases are not as likely to be prosecuted, reporting tends to be lower because victims or witnesses basically assume that reporting won't make any difference.

- In the United States, there are some federal crime laws, but states and smaller jurisdictions can add to those and develop their own legislation—as long as federal law allows that provision.

Burglary

- The FBI and UN statistics are framed in more general ways that are reasonably consistent. For example, regardless of local laws, for purposes of presenting statistics, the FBI defines burglary as "the unlawful entry of a structure to commit a felony or theft."

- They make sure that it's clear that the term "structure" also includes offices, apartments, and house trailers or houseboats—if they're used as a residence—barns, stables, railroad cars, boats and ships. The FBI report further breaks burglary statistics into those where there was attempted forced entry, called forcible entry, and where there was no force, called unlawful entry.

- In the UN Survey, "burglary" includes thefts from homes, factories, shops, offices, or military establishments and thefts using false keys—but excludes thefts from a car, vending machine, parking meter, fenced outdoor area, or container. The UN report states that in most countries, the majority of thefts happen at businesses and corporations, not in homes.

Motor-Vehicle Theft

- Definitions of motor-vehicle theft vary between the FBI report and the UN survey to some degree, but both note this as its own brand of theft.

- Motives behind stealing cars vary. Sometimes, the vehicle is taken for a short time and abandoned later—after joyriding or using the car in connection with another crime; other times, the thief wants to use the car for his or her own transportation. Some vehicles are stolen specifically to resell, in whole or as parts, somewhere else.

In statistics from the FBI and the U.N., auto theft isn't included in the burglary category because it's in its own category of crime.

- According to victimization surveys, motor-vehicle theft is likely to be reported to police, mainly because of the value of the vehicles involved. In developed countries, especially due to insurance, it's estimated that 80% to 90% of vehicle thefts are reported.

- Not surprisingly, the highest rates of motor-vehicle theft are in developed countries, where there are simply more vehicles to steal. As other countries become more developed, they will likely have more thefts.

- Conversely, as new car security systems in developed countries get better at deterring theft, those areas may experience a decreasing trend. It's also possible that as car security systems become more advanced, the way that vehicles are stolen may change.

Arson

- With regard to arson, the UN doesn't report on incendiary fires, but the FBI does. The FBI also gives statistics on larceny thefts that the UN doesn't.

- Examples of those offenses include shoplifting, pickpocketing, stolen car parts, and bicycle theft as well as attempts to commit any of those crimes. Larceny doesn't include embezzlement, forgery, check fraud, and the general class of schemes called con games.

Robbery
- Robbery is taken out of the realm of property crime because it's committed with violence or the threat of violence. Robbery includes muggings, purse snatchings, bank or business holdups, and similar offenses—including carjacking.

- In some countries, the distinction between robbery and a lesser charge is based on the monetary value of what's taken, but overall, the definition of robbery is pretty comparable from country to country. The amount of reported robberies is thought to be fairly close to the number of actual robberies because of both the property loss and the possible trauma—physical or psychological—caused to the victims.

- The UN statistics show that, in general, the more robberies there are in an area, the more other crimes take place there, too. The same is true for robberies and drug-related crime in the United States.

Assault
- Assault, as defined by the UN Survey, means any bodily attack that is not of a sexual nature. Comparison among countries is difficult because in some places, the definition includes the mere threat of bodily harm, and others count punching or slapping, but some places only charge assault if there are visible injuries.

- FBI statistics report aggravated assaults in their summary.

Rape
- Both the FBI and the UN collect data on rape. Two-thirds of the countries that responded to the UN said they concur with a definition of rape as "sexual intercourse without valid consent." The other third of reporting countries either include attempted rapes

or sexual assaults in their rape data or have legal definitions of rape that do not count male victims.

- Robberies, assaults, and rapes all leave eyewitnesses as well as some transfer of physical evidence, but eyewitness accounts can be notoriously inaccurate—especially when the victim is confronted with a weapon. Also, in all 3 of those cases, how quickly a victim comes forth plays a big role in what kind of interview or physical evidence might be collected.

- An interview of a witness's account and a physical exam to see his or her injuries can be undertaken even in the most basic of hospital or police settings, but the ability to collect the only individuating evidence belonging to an attacker—his or her DNA—will depend on the technology available in that area.

Kidnapping
- The UN survey's definition of kidnapping is complex, and not all countries would use the same criteria.

- A kidnapping may leave little evidence behind—especially if a person is just grabbed in a public place and put in a vehicle. Only if and when a victim or suspect—or maybe a related location—is identified could other evidence be collected to tie the suspect to the crime.

Homicide
- Homicide is considered the best overall indicator for the rates of all other violent crimes. When you think about comparing worldwide rates of homicides, you have to consider that advances in medicine in North America, Western Europe, and other developed countries dramatically increase survival rates for what might easily be a homicide somewhere else.

- Victims are far more likely to be killed by people they know than strangers. Research shows that the rate of homicides involving family members or close relatives and associates stays fairly stable or changes very slowly over a long period of time.

- When you see high homicide rates, authorities attribute much of the increase to things like drug trafficking, organized crime, and gang-related violence.

- Apparently, the more widespread firearms are in an area, the more homicides will take place there. The availability of guns, though, is no predictor of the availability of opportunities to examine the evidence that comes from them.

Forensic Crime Labs

- In the United States, there are several large forensic labs at the federal level, but most states have one or more crime labs that also offer a comprehensive range of forensic services.

- Regardless of size or jurisdiction, all forensic labs need an intake system to receive evidence and to ensure a good chain of custody. It's typical today that labs have computerized evidence management systems and barcode technology that can be scanned at every step of evidence testing throughout the lab.

- Forensic labs also need secure storage areas—smaller lockup rooms for some types of evidence, but maybe even a warehouse or garage for processing vehicles. If they do firearms analyses, they need a large tank of water, or other type of chamber, where they can test-fire weapons for comparison.

- Increasing scrutiny is putting even greater demands for accountability on crime labs in the United States. There are lab certification agencies, such as the American Society of Crime Laboratory Directors (ASCLaD), and some states have mandated that all their labs be so certified.

"Arson."

Statistics Canada, "Police-Reported Crime for Selected Offences."

Questions to Consider

1. Is the United Nations involved in the analysis of criminal activity?

2. What is the difference between property crime and violent crime?

3. What are the major categories of property crimes?

4. How is forensic science used in the analysis of property crimes?

Crimes—Nobody's Supposed to Get Hurt
Lecture 33

This lecture will help you apply your knowledge of crime scenes, evidence, forensic labs, and how investigators analyze cases to some real cases. When investigating a crime, investigators first take a careful accounting of the surroundings whenever suspicious or outright illegal circumstances are noted. Some illegal acts, such as drunk driving, don't have a specific victim while other illegal acts—such as identity theft, kidnapping, and arson—do involve a specific victim and possibly endanger other members of society.

Drunk Driving

- Blood alcohol content (BAC) can be figured out by the Widmark formula, named after the Swedish physician who established it, using the following fraction: The numerator is the product of the alcohol consumed in ounces times the percent alcohol in the beverage times a numerical constant of 5.14. Then, that number is put over a denominator of the weight of the person in pounds times a constant factor of 0.73 for men or 0.66 for women.

When police officers notice someone driving erratically, they will stop the car to see if the driver is intoxicated.

- Beer is typically 6% alcohol, so 0.06 would be the decimal, and wine is usually about 12% alcohol, so use 0.12 for wine. The proof of liquor varies, but its percent alcohol is 1/2 its proof, so if you're drinking 100-proof bourbon, the decimal would be 0.5.

- The Widmark calculation doesn't take time into account. In fact, it assumes someone did all the drinking at once. However, you can modify your calculation by estimating the hours since the drinking started, multiplying the number of hours by 0.015, and then subtracting that from the BAC calculation.

- Other factors to take into account are that alcohol absorption is greater on an empty stomach and that these calculations assume an empty stomach. In addition, alcohol is absorbed faster when it's mixed with carbonated beverages—although people tend to ultimately drink slower when they use a mixer in a cocktail.

A Case of Identity Theft

- In 1982, a 3-year-old boy named Jason Robert Evers was kidnapped from Cincinnati by 17-year-old Adrian Williams. Jason was murdered, and Williams was convicted and sentenced to 14–50 years for involuntary manslaughter and kidnapping.

- In 2010, 28 years after Jason's murder, special agents with the U.S. State Department—using a computerized records data-mining identity theft and anti-terrorism program called Operation Death Match—discovered that a man going by the name of Jason Robert Evers was working in Oregon for the State Liquor Control Commission.

- This Oregon Jason Evers had the same birth date and the same parents' first and last names as the 3-year-old who had been murdered. After authorities verified this as a stolen identity, "Jason" was arrested and charged with falsifying a passport and identity theft. However, he refused to tell the authorities his real name, saying that he feared for his safety.

- Somehow, in 1996, "Daniel Kaiser" obtained the real Jason Robert Evers's birth certificate—which listed his birth date and parents' names—and that, in turn, made it possible for him to get a Social Security card.

- In 2002, "Jason Evers" used his birth certificate and Social Security card to apply for a passport and then moved to Portland, Oregon, when he was hired as an inspector by the Oregon Liquor Control Commission. Evers passed a criminal background and fingerprint check, but liquor control officials didn't verify his credentials when he was hired because the company Evers listed as a reference was no longer in business.

- "Jason" was really Doitchin Krastev, born in Sofia, Bulgaria, in 1973 during Communist rule. His parents were prominent Bulgarian intellectuals who wanted a better life for their son. An attorney for the U.S. Office of Management and Budget and his physician wife met Krastev and his parents while they were in Bulgaria studying the effects of Communism, and they proposed that the Krastev teenager move to live with them in Virginia.

- In the 1990s, while attending Davidson College in North Carolina, Krastev called his U.S. host family and told them he wanted to drop out of college. After that, he disappeared completely and, apparently, became Daniel Kaiser.

- Krastev pled guilty in 2010 to passport fraud and identity theft, for which he was sentenced to 2 years in prison. At his sentencing hearing in 2011, Krastev said that he took Jason Evers's name after reading a newspaper article about the murdered 3-year-old, around the time the boy's killer had the possibility of parole.

- Ohio has an open records law, which—shockingly—allows anyone to get a certified copy of anyone else's birth certificate, as long as they have the name and birth date. State Department officials call a birth certificate a breeder document because it's the gateway to all other forms of identification.

A Case of Kidnapping

- Charles Urschel was born in Hancock County, Ohio, in 1890. He married into a family that had gotten rich in the oil boom, and by the early 1930s, he and his second wife, Berenice, were one of the wealthiest couples in Oklahoma City.

- On Saturday, July 22, 1933, Urschel, his friend Walter Jarrett, and their wives were playing bridge on the front porch of the Urschel home when onto the porch walked George "Machine Gun" Kelly and an accomplice, Albert Bates. The pair abducted Charles Urschel at gunpoint.

- As soon as Kelly left, Berenice Urschel contacted the local police and was told to immediately call J. Edgar Hoover at the FBI in Washington DC. Hoover wanted to make an example of this case, and by Monday morning, the crime made headline news across the country.

- A few days after the kidnapping, Kelly's wife and accomplice, Kathryn, met with a local detective friend to try and establish an alibi, but when the detective saw the red dirt on her car tires and an Oklahoma newspaper on the front seat, he got suspicious and phoned the FBI with the tip that Machine Gun Kelly could be the kidnapper. Police showed Mrs. Urschel a mug shot of George Kelly, and she positively identified him as the man who took her husband at gunpoint.

- The day after the kidnapping, Urschel was taken from Oklahoma to a ranch in Paradise, Texas, that was owned by Kathryn Kelly's stepfather. There, he was held captive for over a week at a farmhouse and several other buildings on the ranch, blindfolded most of the time.

- Charles Urschel memorized everything he possibly could about the things around him, and he counted footsteps as he was moved from place to place to calculate distances. Later in the week, the kidnappers attached a chain to Urschel's handcuffs, allowing him to move around the room. Urschel put his fingerprints on anything and everything he could get his hands on—to prove he'd been there.

- Eight days after the kidnapping, Urschel's family paid the demanded ransom of $200,000, which would be over $3.3 million today. The bills were marked, meaning that the FBI recorded all the serial numbers and would have a way to trace them if they appeared in circulation again. A friend of Urschel's made the drop in Kansas City, and his description of the man who took the money from him matched Machine Gun Kelly.

- Urschel was driven to just outside of Oklahoma City, where he was dropped off at a gas station, given $10, and told to call a cab. Urschel made it home on July 31 and immediately started working with the FBI.

- Investigators looked for connections to Kelly and found that Kathryn Kelly's mother and stepfather lived in Paradise. By August 5, the ransom money started showing up. The FBI arrested 5 men in Minneapolis-St. Paul who told them that Kelly had given them the cash.

- On August 10, an FBI agent posing as an inspector went to the ranch. He was able to identify all the information that Urschel had gathered while he was held hostage there. Two days later, the ranch and farmhouse were raided, and accomplices were arrested, including Kelly's in-laws.

- The Kellys crisscrossed the country over the next month, but finally, with the help of an informant, the Kellys were arrested on September 26, 1933, in Memphis, Tennessee. The next day, $73,250 of the marked ransom money was dug up from where it was buried on Kathryn Kelly's uncle's farm outside of Coleman, Texas.

- About $80,000 has never been accounted for. On October 12, 1933, George and Kathryn Kelly were both found guilty and were sentenced to life in prison.

A Case of Arson

- During the 1980s and 1990s, a series of fires were set in California in the Los Angeles area, ranging as far north as Fresno and as far south as Long Beach. The arsonist's M.O. was to use an incendiary timing device. In a few cases, the device was placed in a small foam rubber pillow that would smolder until the fire caught. This led to the arsonist's nickname of "The Pillow Pyro."

- Sometimes, the devices were placed in stores during business hours and with customers inside. The worst of these incidents occurred on October 10, 1984, at a hardware store in a South Pasadena shopping center. Four people died, and the store was completely destroyed.

- The day after the fire, arson investigators from all over the southern part of California came to the store to determine the cause of the fire. Although one investigator—Glendale Fire Department's John Orr—insisted that the cause was arson, the investigative report said that the cause was electrical.

- After many other fires in the area, Captain Marvin G. Casey of the Bakersfield Fire Department began to suspect that the perpetrator might actually be an arson investigator from the LA area. They were able to recover a single fingerprint from one of the time-delay igniters—but without a suspect, they weren't able to match the print to anyone.

- Eventually, LA task-force investigators matched the print to none other than 17-year Glendale Fire Department veteran Captain John Orr—the only fire investigator to insist that the lethal 1984 hardware store fire was arson.

- During April of 1991, as the task-force members sifted through each scenario, they quietly collected evidence. Then, the Bureau of Alcohol, Tobacco, Firearms and Explosives began a sting operation in May of 1991 by installing a tracking device behind the dashboard of Orr's city vehicle, which Orr removed without comment. The tracking device was again installed in November when Orr brought it in for routine servicing. At the next suspicious fire, the tracker proved that Orr was present at the scene, and in December of 1991, a grand jury handed down an indictment.

- After his arrest, the evidence for the lethal hardware store fire was reinvestigated, and Orr was charged with arson. In July of 1992, a federal jury convicted Orr of 3 counts of arson and sentenced him to 3 consecutive 10-year prison terms. In March 1993, he pled guilty to 3 more counts of arson.

- Estimates are that Orr probably set nearly 2000 fires between 1984 and 1991 when he was caught. Apparently, Orr had wanted to move up the ranks at the LA fire department but couldn't get hired there, and he thought that the only way to do so was to show his near superhuman powers of solving arsons on the Glendale force. Despite pleading guilty at his numerous court convictions, Orr strangely continues to maintain that he's innocent.

Crimes—Killers of One, Killers of Many
Lecture 34

This lecture examines 4 cases, in which one or more different types of forensic evidence were responsible for closing the case and bringing the killers to justice for the crimes that they committed against the victims and their families. These cases are just a handful of examples that show the power of forensic evidence and sound investigation in solving homicides, whether the perpetrator takes one life or kills many people over a string of years.

The Case of Roy Whiting

- On July 1, 2000, 8-year-old Sarah Payne was playing hide-and-seek with her brothers and sister in a cornfield near their grandparents' house in West Sussex, England, when she went missing. Sarah's older brother, Lee, told police he saw a "scruffy-looking man with yellowish teeth" in a white van drive down the lane, turn around, and head back toward where Lee was standing.

- The family searched the area, and when they couldn't find Sarah, they contacted police. A witness called police to corroborate that a white van sped down the lane and ran a stop sign on the night of the abduction.

- The next day, a convicted sex offender named Roy Whiting was visited by Sussex police, who were interviewing all sex offenders in the area. Whiting's home was only about 5 miles from Sarah's disappearance, and he had a white van. Officers were suspicious of Whiting's behavior during the interview and kept his home under observation. As soon as he thought police were gone, Whiting attempted to leave—and based on that, he was arrested.

- Although police found a gas-station receipt in his van that threw Whiting's alibi into suspicion, they found nothing at his home to show that Sarah had been there, and they released him after 2 days.

- Sixteen days after Sarah Payne disappeared, a farmer clearing his field of weeds found the nude body of a girl in a shallow grave that was about 15 miles from where Sarah was last seen. DNA testing was done on muscle tissue from the body, and a reference sample was taken from a baby tooth that Sarah's mother had kept, and there was a positive association.

- When new witnesses said that they saw a white van near the farm on the night of the abduction, Whiting was rearrested. Ultimately, investigators seized the white van and did a thorough forensic examination. Over 500 bits of trace evidence—including hundreds of fibers and 40 hairs—gathered from the van and Sarah's body closed the case.

- In December of 2001, Whiting was convicted of the abduction and murder of Sarah Payne and was sentenced to life in prison. Immediately after his conviction, there were renewed calls for greater public access to the UK Home Office's sex offender registry, and the system was rolled out to cover all of England and Wales in 2011 under Sarah's Law.

The Case of Dr. Jeffrey MacDonald

- In the early morning of February 17, 1970, Dr. Jeffrey MacDonald, a surgeon and Green Beret stationed at Fort Bragg, North Carolina, made an emergency phone call to base dispatchers, reporting a stabbing at his home. When 4 military police officers arrived, they found MacDonald lying on the floor of the master bedroom—alive but with a mild concussion, cuts and bruises on his face and chest, and a small, sharp stab wound on his torso.

- MacDonald's wife, Colette, who had been over 5 months pregnant with their third child, was lying dead next to MacDonald with her husband's torn pajama top wadded over her chest. The word "pig" was written in blood on the headboard of the bed. An autopsy later determined Colette had been bludgeoned, both of her arms had been broken, and she was stabbed 21 times with an ice pick and 16 times with a knife. The MacDonald daughters were also found stabbed to death in their respective beds.

- MacDonald told investigators that he had slept on the living room couch that night because his wife had allowed the children to sleep in their bed. He woke up later to hear his wife screaming, and as he got off the couch to help, 3 men attacked him. A fourth intruder, a woman, was chanting, "Acid is groovy; kill the pigs."

- MacDonald said that the 3 men attacked him with a large piece of wood and an ice pick, and when his pajama top got pulled over his head and onto his wrist, he was able to use it as a shield against the ice pick. Eventually, he was knocked unconscious, only to wake up later next to his wife in the bedroom.

- The U.S. Army's Criminal Investigative Division (CID) didn't believe MacDonald's story, and less than 3 months later, the Army charged him with the murder of his wife and daughters.

- Underneath the headboard, where the word "pig" had been written in blood, were fragments of surgical gloves—identical to gloves Dr. MacDonald kept in the kitchen. An ice pick, a paring knife, and a 31-inch piece of lumber were found just outside the back door of the home. All 3 were later determined not only to be the murder weapons, but also to have come from inside the home.

- All 4 of the family members had different blood types, so investigators were able to use bloodstain patterns to trace their movements and figure out what probably happened. The theory is that a fight between MacDonald and his wife began in the master bedroom and then escalated into Dr. MacDonald killing his entire family.

- During his trial, which started in 1979, forensic technicians testified that the shape of the ice pick holes in MacDonald's pajama top had been made when the cloth was not in motion, making it unlikely they were made during his fight with intruders. Using dramatic demonstrative evidence, forensics showed that if the shirt was folded in just the right way, all 48 holes in it could have been made with 21 stabbing motions that precisely matched the 21 ice pick wounds on Colette, who was found with the shirt wadded on top of her.

- MacDonald was convicted on 3 counts of murder and was given a life sentence for each, to be served consecutively. DNA testing was done in 2000, and every hair that was tested matched a member of the MacDonald family—except for one, for which no match has been found.

The Case of Donald Harvey

- In 1987, a 44-year-old patient named John Powell at Cincinnati's Drake Memorial Hospital died. This was surprising because—although Powell had been in a coma following a motorcycle accident—he was showing signs of improvement.

- When pathologist Dr. Lehman performed an autopsy on the body of John Powell, he smelled cyanide and suspected that Powell had been poisoned.

- Authorities began to question Powell's family and friends, but that didn't lead to a motive or any other suspicions. Next, they began to look at Drake Hospital personnel—specifically those who had access to Powell's room. Employees were given the option to voluntarily take a lie detector test. One nurses' aide was on the list but called in sick the day the test was scheduled.

- That employee was 35-year-old Donald Harvey, who friends at work jokingly called "The Angel of Death" because he always seemed to be near when patients died. Immediately, investigators put their full efforts into Harvey, and a search warrant was quickly issued for Harvey's apartment. They found over 30 pounds of cyanide, arsenic, books on poisons and the occult, and Harvey's diary that detailed some of his murders.

- In connection with Powell's death, Harvey was arrested and held on one count of aggravated murder. Investigators began looking at other mysterious deaths at Drake. Hospital employees, who had previously suspected Harvey, began to talk to a news reporter, who was able to show that there was a pattern between deaths and Harvey's work schedule. Bodies of patients who had died were exhumed, and toxicology detected more poisonings.

- To avoid Ohio's death penalty, Harvey tried to plea bargain. He confessed to committing 33 murders between 1970 and 1987. Later, Harvey said that his true number of victims was actually 87. A mental evaluation concluded that—although he did have a history of head trauma and was a victim of sexual abuse—Harvey was sane and competent to stand trial.

- These were not all mercy killings. He did say that he felt terribly sorry for most of these people, but ultimately admitted that he sometimes took patients' lives because he was mad at them for specific things they did.

- Harvey was convicted of a total of 36 counts of aggravated murder and one count of voluntary manslaughter, for which he is currently serving a life sentence.

The Case of Dennis Rader
- In 1974, the Otero family was being stalked in Wichita, Kansas. In broad daylight, the phone lines were cut, their home was entered, and the entire family was murdered.

- The perpetrator was organized and brought the things he needed for these gruesome executions with him. He left a trail of semen throughout the house—but none of the victims were sexually assaulted.

- Nine months after the killings, a reporter at *The Wichita Eagle* received a phone call, allegedly from the Otero family's murderer. The caller directed the reporter to a textbook on mechanical engineering on a shelf in the Wichita Public Library. Stuck in the book was a letter claiming responsibility for the Otero murders and assuring that there would be more killings.

- That contact brought investigators into what would become a hideous 30-year game of cat and mouse with a serial killer. He asked to go by the code name BTK, an acronym that described his predatory sexual fantasies, which were to bind, torture, and kill.

- The trail went cold throughout the early 1980s, though investigators continued to analyze the cases that they believed were linked for any additional clues, and they found some.

- BTK was strangely silent to the media and police throughout the 1990s, and the investigation again went cold—that is, until something drove the killer to reconnect with police. In 2004, through another letter to *The Wichita Eagle*, he claimed responsibility for a 1986 killing. Authorities continued to taunt and communicate with the BTK killer through the media, hoping to bring him closer to the surface.

- Eventually, BTK wrote to police and asked if it was possible to trace the author of a document from a computer disc. Communicating through an ad in the newspaper, investigators lied and told him that it was not possible. The killer sent authorities a floppy disc, and when they performed a metadata search on it, they were able to recover a computer identity name of Dennis and also found information that pointed to a Lutheran Church.

- Using just 4 key words on the Internet—"Dennis," "Wichita," "Lutheran," and "Church"—they were immediately directed to Dennis Rader, who was president of a Lutheran Church in town—not to mention a married man who was the father of 2 children and a leader for the Boy Scouts of America.

Applications—Mass-Disaster Forensics
Lecture 35

T he death of one person can be devastating not only to a family, but even to a community, and mass and serial killers may take several or many people's lives—either at once or over a period of years. Forensic techniques are used to solve crimes involving death, but forensic scientists are often involved in mass disasters, too. "Mass disaster" is a catchall term that includes natural calamities such as earthquakes, floods, volcanoes, and tsunamis—as well as man-made events such as genocides, bombings, and fires. Ecological disasters, such as oil spills, are also classified as mass disasters.

Mass Disasters and Fatalities
- In general, from a forensic perspective, an event called a mass disaster typically implies a large loss of human life over a relatively short span of time.

- The forensic science that is applied mainly involves examining the causes and effects of these types of devastating events—especially to figure out whether criminal charges or civil lawsuits will go before courts—and identifying the large numbers of people who can perish in these catastrophes and figuring out why they died.

- From a professional standpoint, an incident called a mass fatality is usually considered something that causes more deaths than the local law enforcement, emergency, and forensic resources can handle.

Natural Disasters
- The type of natural disaster that is the deadliest is floods. The tsunami in the Indian Ocean in 2004 caused the deaths of over 230,000 people.

- The 7.0 earthquake in Haiti in 2010 caused a loss of life nearly equal to that of the 2004 tsunami—although high poverty and poor building materials were partly responsible for the tremendous number of fatalities and the difficulties in rescuing victims.

- Other natural disasters where victims are hard to find and/or identify include cyclones and hurricanes. In 1999, mudslides that followed a massive rain in Venezuela took the lives of over 15,000 victims.

- Conversely, droughts that cause famines are other natural disasters that will leave victims emaciated but presumably identifiable. In 1932 and 1933, a famine in Russia is estimated to have killed about 5 million people. This was partly a man-made disaster, though, because Stalin controlled crops and food production, which contributed to the massive loss of life.

- In modern mass fatalities from natural causes, looking at engineering issues of structural collapse is important because it has the potential to lead to designs for safer buildings, dams, and bridges that might better withstand future earthquakes, hurricanes, and other unavoidable and sometimes unpredictable events.

Floods are the deadliest type of natural disaster. It's estimated that 3,700,000 people died in a great flood in China in 1931.

- Other analytical sciences will also be involved—depending on the type of disaster—such as geologists, meteorologists, or even microbiologists if the cause is epidemic. Policies related to prevention, intervention, and emergency treatment and relief may also change based on the analyses of natural disasters.

- It's sometimes difficult to separate the natural and man-made components of many mass disasters because there are frequently overlapping issues related to building construction, politics, and population density.

Man-Made Disasters
- The man-made disaster that has led to the greatest loss of life is war. World War I is estimated to have resulted in the loss of 15–65 million people, but that included deaths from the Spanish flu epidemic, which was rampant among soldiers in 1918 and 1919. World War II killed about 40–72 million people—an estimated 2% to 3% of the total world population at the time. About 5–11 million of those deaths were caused by genocide during the Holocaust.

- Other man-made disasters involve the release of toxic chemicals into the air or water from technology. The Chernobyl nuclear plant meltdown in northern Ukraine in 1986 was a serious mass disaster, in which at least 6,500,000 people were exposed to the radiation.

- Fires and explosion—both accidental and intentional—are other forms of man-made mass disasters. The deadliest man-made fire- and explosion-related mass disaster in U.S. history was the September 11, 2001, hijacking of 4 airplanes, 2 of which were flown into the World Trade Center in New York City. A third plane was taken over by passengers and went down in a field in Pennsylvania, and a fourth plane intentionally crashed into the Pentagon building by the hijackers. An estimated 2753 deaths were attributed to this coordinated act of terrorism.

- Our modes of mass transportation have certainly contributed to mass disasters. The steamboat *Sultana* exploded and sank on the

Mississippi River in 1865, killing a minimum of 30 more people than the famous *Titanic*.

- As technology has advanced to include bigger planes, aircraft crashes have increased the death tolls. The worst airline accident prior to 9/11 in the United States was the 1979 crash of an American Airlines plane shortly after it took off from Chicago O'Hare International Airport and lost an engine; 273 people died in that crash.

Responding to Mass Disasters

- In a sense, any mass-disaster setting is a monumental crime scene, and any—if not all—of the forensic techniques and technologies that have been discussed may come into play.

- Just as with a small crime scene, there are safety and security issues for emergency personnel and other first responders, and the area involved has to be secured—to keep others from harm and to prevent looting or damage of evidence.

- Victims need to be tended to—whether injured or dead—while at the same time, proper protocols have to be used to collect any evidence that might aid the incident's investigation. Ultimately, the site must be cleaned up and made usable again, if that's even possible.

- Depending on the mechanism that causes a disaster—or the particular mode of transportation that's involved—the response will differ. The type of public place where an incident occurs—such as an airport, a football stadium, or a university—will also affect how the scene is handled.

- When a catastrophe occurs, the first thing that has to be determined is who is in charge, and you'd be surprised how complicated this can be at times. Often, politics are involved, and entities either want the responsibility for the emergency—sometimes for the prestige it brings them—or prefer to hand off the disaster to anyone who will take over.

- All geographic areas typically already have emergency management systems in place—such as police, fire, and emergency medical personnel.

- Local hospitals are made ready for impending wounded victims, and ambulance and fire companies begin to report their estimated time of arrival to transport victims. These rescuers need to have the personal protective gear and other equipment necessary to transport victims and recover the dead. They may be facing biohazards like body fluids or toxins like jet fuel and many other dangers.

- Secure communication networks have to be quickly set up that will allow only those involved to monitor the information going between police, emergency workers, and the disaster management personnel. The media also has to be managed; they can be a disaster's greatest resource at times, but can also turn into its worst nightmare.

- The necessary equipment has to be quickly procured—whether that involves heavy equipment to remove rubble, search and rescue dogs, or refrigerated trucks to store bodies until autopsy.

- There are also financial concerns, such as who is going to pay disaster workers if they aren't volunteers as well as purchase the necessary supplies.

- In addition, mass fatalities always require establishing a family assistance center. Immediately after a mass fatality is known about, people whose loved ones were on the plane or in the building that collapsed quickly descend on the area to seek news about the victims.

- Part of any emergency plan is to bring in social workers and clergy members to help the grieving. At the same time, computer operators can start to collect antemortem information about victims from the families to assist in identification—such as their appearance and available medical or dental records as well as family reference samples for DNA testing.

- If the incident is a plane crash, the airline involved will deal with public and family concerns. All airline carriers have disaster teams already in place among their staff.

- Often, the disaster management personnel will secure a nearby hotel to house the family members away from the site and to keep them from seeing or overhearing things that may be too much for them to bear.

- Because forensic science is more involved with the dead than the living in these situations, forensic scientists are the ones that deal with the morgue operations. Depending on the proximity to one or more major coroner's or medical examiner's facilities, a temporary morgue may need to be set up in the area.

- In the morgue, depending on the condition of bodies and body parts that come in, autopsies are conducted to establish cause of death and to gather particulars that will assist in identification, such as tattoos or dental work.

- The psychological needs of disaster workers have to also be addressed. The things that they see, hear, and smell can be horrific, and even the most experienced morgue workers can be challenged in a mass-disaster setting.

- Investigating the cause of a disaster might require the expertise of forensic engineers, accident reconstruction experts, fire and explosives investigators, or others—depending on the incident. Figuring out what happened can also involve black-box data recorders or surveillance equipment that may hold information.

- Away from the site, the investigation could also employ high-tech analyses of digital and financial data, particularly if the cause may have been terrorism. Passenger or building occupant lists may need to be accessed to figure out who the victims are likely to be and how many may still be missing. Establishing fault, or potential safety violations that led to the disaster, will have legal implications.

- Cleaning up the site can be a massive and hazardous operation that can take weeks, months, years, or even longer—depending on the extent of the property or environmental damage. Decisions will need to be made about the disposing of any remaining biomass, which is the unidentified human tissue that may be commingled with soil or other contaminants. Biomass needs to be contained, incinerated, or buried.

DMORT

- The first mass disaster that was ever handled by the Disaster Mortuary Operational Response Teams (DMORT), the United States' network of disaster and mortuary teams, happened in 1993 in Hardin, Missouri, when the Missouri River flooded its banks—displacing about 650 coffins and vaults from the Hardin Cemetery, which dated back to 1828. This was an unusual mass disaster because the victims were already dead and buried—as known individuals—but due to the flood, they were scattered as unknown individuals for miles after the waters receded.

- Amazingly, bodies were in all states of preservation when the waters receded: There were mummified remains of people from the 19th century caught up in the branches of trees, visually recognizable embalmed bodies that family members identified after recovery, and bones that were scattered throughout the county.

- It took a dedicated DMORT team of pathologists, anthropologists, and other forensic experts months to try to identify the dead all over again, and many ended up being buried in common caskets without identification.

Suggested Reading

Black, Sunderland, Hackman, and Mallett, eds, *Disaster Victim Identification*.

Guiberson, *Disasters*.

Haglund and Sorg, eds, *Advances in Forensic Taphonomy*.

Hayes and the editors of *Popular Mechanics*, *What Went Wrong*.

Thompson and Black, eds, *Forensic Human Identification*.

Questions to Consider

1. What kinds of natural and man-made events constitute mass disasters?

2. Can you think of specific examples of natural versus man-made mass disasters in recent history?

3. How is forensic science used in mass-fatality contexts?

Applications—Identification Matters
Lecture 36

O ur identity—who we are—connects us to our family, our friends, our property, and all parts of our personal history. Without their identity, people who come into the morgue as unknown individuals are destined to either be buried without a name or sit in a storage area indefinitely. The work of forensic scientists can help provide important answers to people who are waiting in that limbo of not knowing. Sometimes, identifying a victim can lead to a perpetrator and possibly to protecting society from a dangerous predator.

NamUs

- The United States' National Institute of Justice project called the National Missing and Unidentified Persons System, also known as NamUs, is a set of 2 databases: One stores information about missing persons provided by people who are looking for them—including family members and law enforcement officers—and the other holds the records of unidentified remains submitted by coroner's and medical examiner's offices throughout the United States.

- In January of 2009, these 2 databases were linked to each other, creating a technological tool to help find missing persons and identify unknown persons. NamUs uses algorithms to generate potential matches. The NamUs system is also publicly accessible, unlike other databases that are available to professionals only.

- Some estimates put the number of missing persons reports in the United States at about 2300 per day, which amounts to over 800,000 per year. Fortunately, many of these people are quickly returned to their families, but there are currently over 100,000 active missing persons cases in the United States, and only just over 9000 of them are currently in the NamUs system.

- Original estimates for unidentified persons in the United States based on data extrapolations suggested that as many as 40,000 sets of unknown remains might be sitting in morgues, anthropology labs, public cemeteries, or even cremated—leaving nothing but paper records of their existence. Those estimates have now been refined because there were far more unresolved cases in the past than there hopefully and probably will be in the future.

- Unknown remains—especially skeletal remains—were historically difficult to identify before DNA technology was developed in the 1980s, and before the existence of national databases. Currently, there are about 8500 unidentified persons cases in the NamUs system, but there are many thousands more that are in the process of being added to the database over time.

- Newer estimates suggest that there will probably be about 500 to 700 new chronically unidentified cases—which are those where local resources have not provided a positive identification within a few months after the victim is discovered—each year in the future.

The Forensic Science of Human Identification

- A person's biological identity is not the same as the pieces of identification that he or she might carry in a wallet or purse, and although a driver's license, a unique piece of jewelry, or any other personal effect might be a huge clue in the effort to establish identity, those things can only provide a presumptive or circumstantial identification—not a positive one.

- A positive identification requires forensic scientists to match unique physical attributes in unknown remains to what's already known about a missing person. Forensic identification involves matching unknown or questioned evidence—in this case, human remains—to known evidence, which either consists of antemortem records or some type of reference sample.

- Establishing positive identity is a daily task in morgues around the world, and each body that is examined is there because the death is suspicious or might relate to criminal activity. Most of the time, the identification is straightforward—especially in cases such as auto accidents or when family members report the death and provide the deceased's identity.

- Unlike what is showed on television, in modern morgues, body viewing is done through a viewing window or by photography; family members aren't traipsing through the autopsy room. However, most positive identifications are still made by having someone who knows the victim visually confirm the identity. In rare instances, there have been mistaken identities by visual confirmation.

- In general, it's easier to identify fresh remains than skeletal remains, but there are plenty of cases where people who would easily be visually recognizable are still unknown.

- There are other cases where traumatic injury results in such damage that a person becomes unrecognizable, such as someone who is hit by a subway train or jumps off a building. If there are no clues from the personal effects, investigators may have no idea where to start.

- A related generalization is that deaths in heavily populated areas are less likely to result in advanced decomposition than when people die or are dumped in remote locations.

- People who are found in the same geographic area where they go missing are typically more quickly identified, and people whose remains are found nearer to the time they disappeared are more likely to be quickly identified than those who have been missing for a long time. Both the missing and the dead side of these investigations must work closely together to resolve cases quickly.

Identifying the Unknown Dead
- There are 3 main categories of methods that are used to identify the unknown dead: soft parts of the body, such as skin; more

durable features, such as bones and teeth; and molecular methods of identification, such as DNA.

- It's still very common that people are visually identified, but other body surface features can also be critical in establishing identity. In the United States, fingerprints can be taken and put into the Integrated Automated Fingerprint Identification System (IAFIS) and the NamUs system—where they can be compared to fingerprint records already on file or archived for future comparisons.

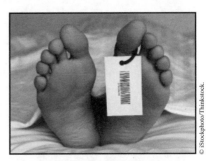

- Unique skin features such as birthmarks, scars, and tattoos can be examined, described, measured, and photographed for dissemination through the media and input into the NamUs system.

The scope of the missing and unidentified persons issue in the United States is astounding.

- Bones and teeth also provide valuable clues in establishing identification. Forensic anthropology techniques can narrow in on an identity by suggesting the age, sex, ancestry, and stature of a person from skeletal remains.

- With the availability of DNA testing, you might think that there's little use for bones or teeth in human identification, but if remains are a complete unknown, an anthropology consult can definitely narrow the search.

- Dental IDs are still pretty common because they're faster and less expensive than DNA testing. Sometimes, dental fillings and bridgework are used to identify unknown persons through comparisons with existing dental records.

- Many types of surgical implants and other medical devices carry serial numbers that can be found in human remains and, through the manufacturer, have the potential of being linked to the surgical patient they were implanted in. Even if those devices don't carry a serial number, they certainly indicate a medical history that can be used to narrow down the field of possibilities when consulting missing persons records.

From Professor Murray's Forensic Files

The following case shows the interdisciplinary nature of forensic science and how it works hand in hand with dedicated law enforcement professionals. It is one of my most extraordinary cases, where teamwork and technology led to a remarkable case of identification after almost 40 years.

On October 11 of 1970 in Darke County, Ohio, 2 teenagers riding horseback through a cornfield found the nude body of a woman. There was no obvious cause of death, but the fact that her naked body had been dumped there suggested that there was foul play. Although investigators worked the case at the time, no leads developed, and several weeks later, the body was buried as a Jane Doe in the county cemetery. In December of 1970, the last entry was made in the case file, and no further actions were taken.

Almost 30 years later, in February of 1999, a young detective from Darke County took an interest in this cold case and decided to reopen it. There were many problems, including the fact that investigators had no autopsy report, no morgue photos, and basically no evidence to work from—only the scant information in the 1970 sheriff's report remained.

On October 6 of 2006—almost 36 years to the day since her body had been originally discovered—the remains of this young Jane Doe were removed from her unmarked grave. Two teeth and a segment of her left thighbone were sent off for DNA analysis. In December of 2006, her skeleton was brought to my lab for an anthropology analysis because, by this time, all that remained was bones.

The victim was a young white female who stood about 5′3″ to 5′7″ tall, and based on only photographs from the initial discovery of her body, I estimated that she had been in the environment for about a week whereas the original sheriff's department report indicated that she had probably been there for close to a month.

In December of 2007, after completing my analysis, I sent the skull to a forensic artist in Tennessee, and she produced a clay facial reconstruction of the young woman. Photos of the artist's work were released to the local media in October of 2008—38 years after the body was found in 1970.

An elderly woman named Phyllis from Darke County saw the image of the young woman in the newspaper and contacted police. She said that the woman resembled her 18-year-old niece, Jeannie, who was last seen getting on a Greyhound bus in Green Bay, Wisconsin, in the late summer of 1970. Jeannie was scheduled to change buses in Chicago and then continue on to Richmond, Indiana, which was the closest Greyhound stop to Darke County. In Richmond, she was to be picked up by Phyllis for a late summer visit with her cousins at Phyllis's home in Darke County.

When Jeannie wasn't found at the bus station, both Phyllis and her sister in Green Bay called their local police offices to report Jeannie missing, but because she was 18 years old, her disappearance was not taken as seriously as her mother and aunt insisted it should.

Phyllis thought that the assumption of the police was that Jeannie had either gotten off the bus in Chicago of her own volition or had possibly been abducted there. In 1970, when the sheriff's office suggested that the woman in the cornfield had been there for about a month, that created a timeline too early for the expected date of Jeannie's arrival, and a link was never made.

In 2008, DNA reference samples were taken from Phyllis, a maternal aunt from Green Bay, and Jeannie's only living sibling, a sister from Green Bay. In 2009, based on mitochondrial DNA comparisons among these maternal relatives—a full 39 years after her disappearance—Jeannie's body was finally positively identified.

Although this is an extremely unusual case of protracted but positive identification, it illustrates how the efforts of law enforcement and forensic science can combine their resources and use powerful technologies to benefit society. Jeannie's case has not been solved, but in finding out who she was, law enforcement is perhaps better equipped to seek justice for her.

Suggested Reading

Black, Sunderland, Hackman, and Mallett, eds, *Disaster Victim Identification*.

Thompson and Black, eds, *Forensic Human Identification*.

Questions to Consider

1. About how many people go missing each day in the United States?

2. What kind of technology is available to help match missing persons to unknown human remains?

3. What is the difference between a presumptive and a positive identification?

4. What specific methods can be used by forensic scientists in attempting to identify unknown persons?

Bibliography

Alison, Lawrence. *Forensic Psychologist's Casebook: Psychological Profiling and Criminal Investigation*. London, England: Willan Publishing, 2005. A case-based book about profiling and forensic investigation.

Almirall, Jose R., and Kenneth G. Furton. *Analysis and Interpretation of Fire Scene Evidence*. Boca Raton, FL: CRC Press, 2004. Advanced reference for arson investigators.

"Arson." Department of Justice, Federal Bureau of Investigation, Criminal Justice Information Services Division. Accessed 14 September, 2011. http://www2.fbi.gov/ucr/cius2009/offenses/property_crime/arson.html. Statistics and information on arson in the United States with links to statistics for other crimes.

Bass, William, and Jon Jefferson. *Death's Acre: Inside the Legendary Forensic Lab the Body Farm Where the Dead Do Tell Tales*. New York: Berkley Books, 2003. A case-based approach to forensic anthropology written by one of the world's most widely known forensic anthropologists, Dr. Bill Bass.

Bevel, Tom, and Ross M. Gardner. *Bloodstain Pattern Analysis with an Introduction to Crime Scene Reconstruction*. 3rd ed. Boca Raton, FL: CRC Press, 2008. An advanced but comprehensive reference book for bloodstain analysts.

Black, Sue, G. Sunderland, L. Hackman, and X. Mallett, eds. *Disaster Victim Identification: Experience and Practice (Global Perspectives of Disaster Victim Identification)*. Boca Raton, Florida: CRC Press, Taylor & Francis Group, 2011. Covers all facets of the use of forensic science in human identification—with particular emphasis on mass disasters—using a case-based approach.

Bodziak, William J. *Footwear Impression Evidence: Detection, Recovery, and Examination.* 2nd ed. Boca Raton, FL: CRC Press, 1999. Detailed overview of footwear impression evidence, including case studies.

———. *Tire Tread and Tire Track Evidence: Recovery and Forensic Examination.* 2nd ed. Boca Raton, FL: CRC Press, 2008. Detailed overview of tire evidence.

Bowers, C. Michael, ed. *Forensic Dental Evidence: An Investigator's Handbook.* 2nd ed. Waltham, MA: Academic Press/Elsevier, 2004. Color-illustrated comprehensive look at the science of forensic odontology.

Brenner, John C. *Forensic Science: An Illustrated Dictionary.* Boca Raton, FL: CRC Press, 2003. Includes the basic terminology of forensics with images and brief explanations.

Burke, Michael P. *Forensic Medical Investigation of Motor Vehicle Incidents.* Boca Raton, FL: CRC Press, 2006. A comprehensive reference on all facets of vehicular accidents—from causes and vehicle technology to injuries, including some graphic illustrations.

Butler, John M. *Advanced Topics in Forensic DNA Typing: Methodology.* Waltham, MA: Academic Press/Elsevier, 2011. Very advanced, but good depth for those with some background in DNA and genetics.

———. *Fundamentals of Forensic DNA Typing.* Waltham, MA: Academic Press/Elsevier, 2009. A good overview of forensic DNA analysis from the scene to the lab, including cases and history.

Caddy, Brian, ed. *Forensic Examination of Glass and Paint: Analysis and Interpretation.* Boca Raton, FL: CRC Press, 2001. An advanced book—for those with a background in chemistry and materials analysis.

Carper, Kenneth L. *Forensic Engineering.* 2nd ed. Boca Raton, FL: CRC Press, 2000. An advanced book—for those with an engineering background. Covers fires, structural failures, and relationships to the legal system.

Carrier, Brian. *File System Forensic Analysis*. Upper Saddle River, NJ: Addison-Wesley Professional, an imprint of Pearson, 2005. An advanced book—for someone with a detailed knowledge of computers and operating systems.

Casey, Eoghan. *Digital Evidence and Computer Crime*. 3rd ed. Waltham, MA: Academic Press/Elsevier, 2011. A textbook that introduces the topic of computer forensics.

Cole, M. D., and B. Caddy. *The Analysis of Drugs of Abuse: An Instruction Manual*. Boca Raton, FL: CRC Press, 1994. A bit dated, but a good textbook that covers all aspects of the forensic analysis of abused drugs, including types and technologies—for those with some chemistry background.

Craig, Emily A. *Teasing Secrets from the Dead: My Investigations at America's Most Infamous Crime Scenes*. New York: Three Rivers Press/Random House, 2005. Forensic anthropology at Waco, Texas (David Koresh cult), the Oklahoma City bombing, and September 11, 2001.

Delatte, Norbert J. *Beyond Failure: Forensic Case Studies for Civil Engineers*. Reston, VA: American Society of Civil Engineers, 2008. A completely case-based look at structural and mechanical failures, including many familiar examples from around the world.

DeNevi, Don, John H. Campbell, Stephen Band, and John E. Otto. *Into the Minds of Madmen: How the FBI's Behavioral Science Unit Revolutionized Crime Investigation*. Amherst, NY: Prometheus Books, 2003. Covers the history and development of profiling.

Douglas, John, and Mark Olshaker. *The Anatomy of Motive*. New York: Simon and Schuster, 1999. Forensic-psychology and profiling stories and history from the FBI's John Douglas.

Eckert, William G., ed. *Introduction to Forensic Sciences*. 2nd ed. Boca Raton, FL: CRC Press, 1996. Was a standard textbook for many years. Contains history and a range of chapters by experts in the field with black-and-white illustrations.

Eisen, Mitchell L., Jodi A. Quas, and Gail S. Goodman. *Memory and Suggestibility in the Forensic Interview*. Oxford, UK: Routledge, 2001. Looks at interview techniques with an emphasis on psychology.

Eliopulos, Louis N. *Death Investigator's Handbook, Vol. 1: Crime Scenes*. Boulder, CO: Paladin Press, 2006. A pretty comprehensive book that covers crime-scene analysis for many different settings where bodies could be found.

————. *Death Investigator's Handbook, Vol. 3: Scientific Investigations*. Boulder, CO: Paladin Press, 2006. Covers numerous disciplines—including odontology, anthropology, toxicology, serology, and firearms—highlighting the many ancillary forensic science analyses that intersect with the work of a death investigator.

Ellen, David. *Scientific Examination of Documents: Methods and Techniques*. 3rd ed. Boca Raton, FL: CRC Press, 2005. An advanced and comprehensive look at the analysis of questioned documents.

Englert, Rod, Kathy Passero, and Ann Rule. *Blood Secrets: Chronicles of a Crime Scene Reconstructionist*. New York: Thomas Dunne Books, 2010. A case-based book that covers a variety of investigations through the autobiographical accounts of investigator and bloodstain expert Rod Englert.

Esherick, Joan. *Criminal Psychology and Personality Profiling*. Broomall, PA: Mason Crest Publishers, 2005. Geared toward young adult readers. Covers only the basics.

Evans, Colin. *The Casebook of Forensic Detection: How Science Solved 100 of the World's Most Baffling Crimes*. New York: Berkley Trade/Penguin Books, 2007. A very basic book that does not provide in-depth coverage but is suitable for young readers and those wanting an introduction to some of these notorious crimes.

Ewing, Charles Patrick. *Minds on Trial: Great Cases in Law and Psychology*. New York: Oxford University Press, 2006. A case-based look at 20 high-profile courtroom dramas from the second half of the 20th century that involve forensic psychology.

Feder, Harold A., and Max M. Houck. *Feder's Succeeding as an Expert Witness.* 4th ed. Boca Raton, FL: CRC Press, 2008. A comprehensive overview of expert testimony in forensic science.

Fisher, Barry A. J. *Techniques of Crime Scene Investigation.* 7th ed. Boca Raton, FL: CRC Press, 2003. Information on many types of evidence as well as techniques for collecting the evidence.

Fisher, Barry A. J., William J. Tilstone, and Catherine Woytowicz. *Introduction to Criminialistics: The Foundation of Forensic Science.* New York: Academic Press/Elsevier, 2009. A general reference textbook that is illustrated with color images but is not as comprehensive as others. It is mainly focused on standard lab analyses and does not include all specialties.

Gaensslen, R. E. *Sourcebook in Forensic Serology, Immunology, and Biochemistry.* Ann Arbor, MI: University of Michigan Library, 1983. Somewhat dated, so it doesn't include the latest technology, but it gives a good and clear introduction to the basics of serology in forensic science.

Garret, Brandon. *Convicting the Innocent: Where Criminal Prosecutions Go Wrong.* Cambridge, MA: Harvard University Press, 2011. An in-depth look at why wrongful convictions happen and what can be done to prevent them in the future.

Gennard, Dorothy E. *Forensic Entomology: An Introduction.* Hoboken, NJ: Wiley, 2007. An introductory textbook on forensic entomology that is suitable for any adult reader.

George, Robert M. *Facial Geometry: Graphic Facial Analysis for Forensic Artists.* Springfield, IL: Charles C. Thomas Publisher, Ltd., 2007. An advanced reference guide for forensic artists.

Gibson, Lois. *Forensic Art Essentials: A Manual for Law Enforcement Artists*. Burlingtonm, MA: Academic Press/Elsevier, 2007. An overview of forensic artistry.

Goff, M. Lee. *A Fly for the Prosecution: How Insect Evidence Helps Solve Crimes*. Cambridge, MA: Harvard University Press, 2001. A case-based book about forensic entomology that is written by one of the best in the field.

Guiberson, Brenda Z. *Disasters: Natural and Man-Made Catastrophes through the Centuries*. New York: Henry Holt & Co., 2010. A coverage of historical disasters that is geared toward younger readers.

Gunn, Alan. *Essential Forensic Biology*. Hoboken, NJ: Wiley, 2006. A comprehensive guide to many uses of biological materials in forensics, including protists, plants, and animals.

Haglund, William D., and Marcella Harnish Sorg, eds. *Advances in Forensic Taphonomy: Method, Theory, and Archaeological Perspectives*. Boca Raton, FL: CRC Press, 2001. Case-based examination of many facets of forensic anthropology including decomposition, water environments, and mass graves.

———. *Forensic Taphonomy: The Postmortem Fate of Human Remains*. Boca Raton, FL: CRC Press, 1997. A case-based examination of decomposition and environmental influences on human remains.

Hanzlick, Randy. *Death Investigation: Systems and Procedures*. Boca Raton, FL: CRC Press, 2007. An inexpensive reference that describes the different systems of death investigation in the United States, the roles of different experts involved, and autopsy procedures.

Harrendorf, Stefan, Markku Heiskanen, and Steven Malby, eds. "International Statistics on Justice and Crime." Helsinki, Finland: European Institute for Crime Prevention and Control (HEUNI), in association with the United Nations Office on Drugs and Crime (UNODC), 2010. A summary and analysis of crime trends for countries and regions around the world—including information on whether country-to-country comparisons are reasonable—covering the areas of homicide; drug-related crime; complex crimes, including organized crime; and statistics for criminal justice systems, including trends in prison populations.

Hayes, William, and the editors of *Popular Mechanics. What Went Wrong: Investigating the Worst Man-Made and Natural Disasters.* New York: Hearst, 2011. Covers the major world disasters from the past 100 years, including natural phenomena and transportation accidents.

Heard, Brian J. *Handbook of Firearms and Ballistics: Examining and Interpreting Forensic Evidence.* 2nd ed. Hoboken, NJ: Wiley, 2008. An advanced and case-based approach to ballistics analysis.

Houck, Max M., and Jay A. Siegel. *Fundamentals of Forensic Science.* 2nd ed. Burlington, MA: Academic Press/Elsevier, 2010. A comprehensive, detailed, and illustrated textbook that covers all the major specialties and uses cases to clarify.

Hunter, William. *DNA Analysis.* Broomall, PA: Mason Crest Publishers, 2005. A good introductory overview of forensic DNA analysis that is geared toward young readers but is suitable for anyone interested in the basics.

Huss, Matthew T. *Forensic Psychology.* Hoboken, NJ: Wiley, 2008. A good general textbook about the field of forensic psychology.

Iserson, Kenneth V. *Death to Dust: What Happens to Dead Bodies?* Tucson, AZ: Galen Press, 1994. A comprehensive look at cultural and scientific aspects of death.

James, Stuart H., and Jon J. Nordby. *Forensic Science: An Introduction to Scientific and Investigative Techniques.* 3rd ed. Boca Raton, FL: CRC Press, 2009. A very detailed and comprehensive textbook with many color illustrations (some quite graphic). Chapters are written by experts in the fields.

James, Stuart H., Paul E. Kish, and T. Paulette Sutton. *Principles of Bloodstain Pattern Analysis: Theory and Practice.* Boca Raton, FL: CRC

Press, 2005. An advanced and comprehensive case-based reference for bloodstain analysts that includes connections to other forensic sciences.

Kranacher, Mary-Jo, Richard Riley, and Joseph T. Wells. *Forensic Accounting and Fraud Examination.* Hoboken, NJ: Wiley, 2010. A fairly advanced book that is geared toward those with a background in accounting who want to learn more about how fraud examinations are carried out.

Kurland, Michael. *How to Solve a Murder: The Forensic Handbook.* New York: MacMillan, 1995. Not written by an expert, but it is a fun and easy read that focuses on the types of criminal and forensic sciences used to analyze homicides using cases and black-and-white line art.

Largo, Michael. *Final Exits: The Illustrated Encyclopedia of How We Die.* New York: HarperCollins, 2006. A somewhat irreverent look at causes of death through the ages.

Lentini, John J. *Scientific Protocols for Fire Investigation.* Boca Raton, FL: CRC Press, 2006. An advanced look at the science, history, and theory of fire scene analysis.

Li, Richard. *Forensic Biology: Identification and DNA Analysis of Biological Evidence.* Boca Raton, FL: CRC Press, 2008. Covers all aspects of serology by providing information on a variety of body fluids and how they are analyzed in forensic laboratories, including a lot of detail about DNA analysis from body fluids and tissues.

Libal, Angela. *Fingerprints, Bite Marks, Ear Prints: Human Signposts.* Broomall, PA: Mason Crest Publishers, 2005. A young-adult read about several types of forensic evidence.

Loftus, Elizabeth F. *Eyewitness Testimony.* Cambridge, MA: Harvard University Press, 1996. Written by one of the world's leading experts on the fallibility of memory.

Lyle, D. P. *Forensics for Dummies*. Hoboken, NJ: Wiley Publishing, Inc., 2004. Not written by a forensic scientist, but it is a fun and easy read with limited black-and-white line art that is suitable for young readers or adults.

Maples, William R., and Michael Browning. *Dead Men Do Tell Tales: The Strange and Fascinating Cases of a Forensic Anthropologist*. New York: Broadway Books, 1995. A case-based book about the work of Dr. Bill Maples.

Marshall, Maurice, and Jimmie C. Oxley. *Aspects of Explosives Detection*. Waltham, MA: Elsevier Science, 2008. An advanced but comprehensive look at the many types of explosives and how experts attempt to detect them, including the use of dogs and high-tech advances.

Meyers, Charles. *Silent Evidence: Firearms (Forensic Ballistics) and Toolmarks*. Boone, NC: Parkway Publishers, 2004. A book that provides case-based coverage of firearms and toolmark analyses.

Molina, D. K. *Handbook of Forensic Toxicology for Medical Examiners*. Boca Raton, FL: CRC Press, 2009. A very advanced book—for those with a pharmacology or medical background.

Murray, Elizabeth. *Death: Corpses, Cadavers, and Other Grave Matters*. Minneapolis, MN: Lerner Publishers, 2010. Offers background information on the science of death and is geared toward young readers but is suitable for anyone with an interest in the topic.

———. *Forensic Identification: Putting a Name and Face on Death*. Minneapolis, MN: Lerner Publishers, forthcoming. Touches on several topics—including fingerprints, anthropology, odontology, serology, and DNA—all geared toward identification. Suitable for young audiences but appropriate for all beginners in the topic.

Napier, Michael R. *Behavior, Truth, and Deception: Applying Profiling and Analysis to the Interview Process*. Boca Raton, FL: CRC Press, 2010. A fairly advanced but comprehensive look at the psychological interview.

Navarro, Joe. *Hunting Terrorists: A Look at the Psychopathology of Terror.* Springfield, IL: Charles C. Thomas Publishers, Ltd., 2005. A book that puts specific emphasis on the theories behind terrorism and how intelligence can be used to seek out terrorists.

Nelson, Bill, Amelia Phillips, and Christopher Steuart. *Guide to Computer Forensics and Investigations.* Boston, MA: Course Technology Books, 2009. An advanced reference that covers many aspects of computers and how investigators analyze computer crimes.

Noon, Randall K. *Engineering Analysis of Fires and Explosions.* Boca Raton, FL: CRC Press, 1995. An advanced and comprehensive look at the forensics of both fires and explosions, including case studies.

———. *Forensic Engineering Investigation.* Boca Raton, FL: CRC Press, 2000. Includes investigations of fires, explosions, vehicle accidents, and more.

———. *Introduction to Forensic Engineering.* Boca Raton, FL: CRC Press, 1992. Covers many applications of engineering in forensic science, including basic and common events such as hail damage, electrical circuitry issues, frozen pipes, and slip-and-fall accidents. Contains lots of information about vehicle accidents and includes equations and examples.

Nuland, Sherwin B. *How We Die: Reflections on Life's Final Chapter.* New York: Vintage Books/Random House, 1993. A scientific, practical, and thorough examination of death and some of its causes.

Osterburg, James W., and Richard H. Ward. *Criminal Investigation: A Method for Reconstructing the Past.* 6th ed. New Providence, NJ: Matthew Bender and Company, 2010. A textbook that is largely aimed at law enforcement and includes comprehensive coverage of how numerous types of crimes are investigated from crime scene to courtroom using both behavioral and physical sciences. Contains limited black-and-white images (some graphic).

Peterson, Julie K. *Understanding Surveillance Technologies: Spy Devices, Privacy, History, & Applications.* 2nd ed. Oxford, UK: Auerbach Publications, an imprint of Taylor & Francis, 2007. An advanced textbook for those with an interest in much greater depth on surveillance devices and related topics.

Petherick, Wayne A., Brent E. Turvey, and Claire E. Ferguson, eds. *Forensic Criminology.* Burlington, MA: Academic Press/Elsevier, 2010. A comprehensive textbook with very limited black-and-white images that is focused on criminalistics and legal issues, including historical contexts.

Prahlow, Joseph. *Forensic Pathology for Police, Death Investigators, Attorneys, and Forensic Scientists.* New York: Humana Press, 2010. An easy-to-understand overview of death investigation, autopsy, postmortem interval, human identification, and many related topics.

Rainis, Kenneth G. *Hair, Clothing, and Tire Track Evidence: Crime-Solving Science Experiments.* Berkeley Heights, NJ: Enslow Publishers, 2006. Uses experiments to teach limited aspects of forensic science and is geared toward young readers.

Ratay, Robert. *Forensic Structural Engineering Handbook.* New York: McGraw-Hill Professional, 2009. An advanced reference—for those with an engineering background.

Redsicker, David R. *The Practical Methodology of Forensic Photography.* 2nd ed. Boca Raton, FL: CRC Press, 2000. A comprehensive textbook covering information about all facets of forensic photography.

Ribowsky, Shiya. *Dead Center: Behind the Scenes at the World's Largest Medical Examiner's Office.* New York: HarperCollins, 2006. Stories from the 15-year career of a death investigator in the New York City Medical Examiner's Office, including during September 11, 2001.

Robertson, James R. *Forensic Examination of Hair.* Boca Raton, FL: CRC Press, 1999. Provides information about DNA analysis and drug testing on hair as well as general principles of forensic hair analysis.

Robinson, Edward M. *Crime Scene Photography*. 2nd ed. Burlington, MA: Academic Press/Elsevier, 2010. A textbook that covers many aspects of crime scene documentation using photography.

Rogers, Richard. *Clinical Assessment of Malingering and Deception*. 3rd ed. New York: The Guilford Press, 2008. An advanced reference for those with a strong background or interest in psychology.

Saferstein, Richard. *Criminalistics: An Introduction to Forensic Science*. 10th ed. Saddle River, NJ: Pearson Prentice Hall, 2010. A basic introductory textbook that does not include all specialties but has good explanations of the bases of chemical, microscopic, and physical analyses—including some case profiles and illustrations.

Scammell, Henry, and Douglas Ubelaker. *Bones: A Forensic Detective's Casebook*. New York: M. Evans and Co., 2000. A case-based book about some of the most noteworthy cases of the Smithsonian's Dr. Doug Ubelaker.

Seaman Kelly, Jan, and Brian S. Lindblom. *Scientific Examination of Questioned Documents*. 2nd ed. Boca Raton, FL: CRC Press, 2006. An advanced but comprehensive reference on all facets of document examination.

Senn, David R., and Paul G. Stimson. *Forensic Dentistry*. 2nd ed. Boca Raton, FL: CRC Press, 2010. A detailed overview of forensic odontology.

Shaw, Mark, Jan van Dijk, and Wolfgang Rhomberg. "Determining Trends in Global Crime and Justice: An Overview of Results from the United Nations Surveys of Crime Trends and Operations of Criminal Justice Systems." *Forum on Crime and Society* 3, nos. 1 and 2, December 2003. A good explanation of the difficulties that can be encountered when comparing different countries' crime statistics. Includes data up to the year 2000 for total crime and specific crimes, such as homicides and robbery.

Shelton, David. *Forensic Science in Court: Challenges in the Twenty-First Century*. Lanham, MD: Rowman & Littlefield, 2010. A comprehensive look at the legal issues surrounding forensic-science and expert-witness issues in court.

Siegel, Jay A., and Kathy Mirakovits. *Forensic Science: The Basics*. 2nd ed. Boca Raton, FL: CRC Press, 2010. A comprehensive and color-illustrated textbook that is suitable for beginners. Covers all major forensic specialties—except the behavioral sciences—and uses cases to clarify. The textbook used in Professor Murray's forensic science course.

Slyter, Steven A. *Forensic Signature Examination*. Springfield, IL: Charles C. Thomas Publisher, Ltd., 1996. An inexpensive textbook that covers handwriting analysis—but not all facets of document examination.

Snyder Sachs, Jessica. *Corpse: Nature, Forensics, and the Struggle to Pinpoint Time of Death*. New York: Basic Books/Perseus Publishing, 2001. Not written by a forensic scientist, but it is an interesting and inexpensive read on a variety of topics related to death and forensic investigation of the dead.

Stauffer, Eric, Julia A. Dolan, and Reta Newman. *Fire Debris Analysis*. Waltham, MA: Academic Press/Elsevier, 2007. A very advanced reference that includes the history of analyses.

Steadman, Dawnie W. *Hard Evidence: Case Studies in Forensic Anthropology*. 2nd ed. Saddle River, NJ: Prentice Hall, 2009. A case-based textbook that illustrates the uses of forensic anthropology.

Tapper, Colin. "Criminal Law Revision Committee 11th Report: Character Evidence." *The Modern Law Review* 36, no. 1 (January 1973): 56–64. Summary of Committee findings on the difficulties of including or excluding eyewitness evidence, particularly in regard to the character of the accused.

Taupin, Jane Moira, and Chesterene Cwiklik. *Scientific Protocols for Forensic Examination of Clothing*. Boca Raton, FL: CRC Press, 2010. This not only covers clothing, but due to its comprehensive nature, also includes information about serology, bloodstain patterns, DNA, soil evidence, protists, plants, and animals as related to the analysis of clothing.

Taylor, Karen T. *Forensic Art and Illustration*. Boca Raton, FL: CRC Press, 2001. A very comprehensive overview of all facets of forensic art.

Thompson, Tim, and Sue Black, eds. *Forensic Human Identification: An Introduction*. Boca Raton, FL: CRC Press, Taylor & Francis Group, 2007. A thorough discussion of all facets of human identification as used in forensic settings and mass disasters.

Tibbett, Mark, and David O. Carter. *Soil Analysis in Forensic Taphonomy: Chemical and Biological Effects of Buried Human Remains*. Boca Raton, FL: CRC Press, 2008. Includes information about decomposition and the effects of burial on the body.

Trestrail, John Harris. *Criminal Poisoning: Investigation Guide for Law Enforcement, Toxicologists, Forensic Scientists, and Attorneys*. New York: Humana Press, 2007. Covers many facets, including the history of poisons, types, and psychology of poisoners.

United Nations Office on Drugs and Crime. "United Nations Surveys on Crime Trends and the Operations of Criminal Justice Systems (CTS)." http://www.unodc.org/unodc/en/data-and-analysis/United-Nations-Surveys-on-Crime-Trends-and-the-Operations-of-Criminal-Justice-Systems.html. Provides crime statistics from around the world—both by country and by region. New surveys are completed every few years.

Walton, Richard H. *Cold Case Homicides: Practical Investigative Techniques*. Boca Raton, FL: CRC Press, 2006. A case-based textbook that covers many intersections between forensic science and the investigation of old homicide cases. A very comprehensive book with good detail that is illustrated in black and white with some color plates.

White, Tim D., and Pieter A. Folkens. *The Human Bone Manual*. Burlington, MA: Academic Press/Elsevier, 2005. A comprehensive guide to the human skeleton, including concepts at the foundation of forensic anthropology.

Why the Towers Fell: An Exclusive Investigation into the Collapse of the World Trade Center. DVD. PBS, NOVA, 2002. An overview of the structural engineering failures that caused the World Trade Center towers to fall after the terrorist attacks on September 11, 2001.

Wong, Raphael C., and Harley Y. Tse. *Drugs of Abuse: Body Fluid Testing.* New York: Humana Press, 2010. Discusses the history and uses of body fluid testing in forensic drug analyses. Contains somewhat advanced content.

Zulawski, David E., Douglas E. Wicklander, Shane G. Sturman, and L. Wayne Hoover. *Practical Aspects of Interview and Interrogation.* 2nd ed. Boca Raton, FL: CRC Press, 2001. Highlights interview and interrogation with emphasis on memory and eyewitness issues.

Internet Resources
American Academy of Forensic Sciences. Accessed March 2, 2012. http://aafs.org. Provides brief descriptions of the various specialties that have sections within the AAFS. Also includes information about careers in forensic sciences and the educational pathways to reach them.

ASTM International. Accessed March 2, 2012. http://www.astm.org. Information on soil testing and on standards and certification for engineering and other disciplines. (ASTM International is formerly known as the American Society for Testing and Materials.)

British Standards Institution. Accessed March 2, 2012. http://www.bsigroup.com. Information on standardized soil testing and for various other disciplines.

Federal Bureau of Investigation. Accessed March 2, 2012. http://www.fbi.gov and http://www.fbi.gov/about-us/cjis/ucr/ucr (Uniform Crime Reports). Shows the breadth of FBI involvement, including Most Wanted lists of criminals and terrorists, information on kidnappings, white-collar crime, crime statistics, and law enforcement in the United States.

Home Office. Accessed March 2, 2012. http://www.homeoffice.gov.uk. Covers the range of issues that the Home Office in the UK is involved in—including immigration, drug-related crime, and counterterrorism—with statistics for individual types of crimes.

Innocence Project. Accessed March 2, 2012. http://www.innocenceproject. org/understand/Eyewitness-Misidentification.php. Details the Innocence Project's goal of using DNA evidence to prove the innocence of individuals who have been wrongfully imprisoned, reasons for wrongful imprisonment, and suggested changes for the court systems to prevent more innocent people from being wrongfully convicted.

Interpol. Accessed March 2, 2012. http://www.interpol.int. Contains individual web pages for the various types of crimes and issues that Interpol deals with, including drug-related crimes, criminal organizations, pharmaceutical crimes, financial and high-tech crimes, intellectual property rights, fugitives, public safety and terrorism, human trafficking, corruption, maritime piracy, and property crimes such as the theft of art and cultural objects.

McCrone Research Institute. Accessed March 2, 2012. http://www.mcri.org/ home. Information on the independent, not-for-profit organization dedicated to teaching and research in light and electron microscopy, crystallography, and ultramicroanalysis.

Royal Canadian Mounted Police. Accessed March 2, 2012. http://www.rcmp-grc.gc.ca. Covers the gamut of issues that the RCMP are involved in, including border security, drug-related crime, firearms, missing children, and human trafficking.

Statistics Canada. "Police-Reported Crime for Selected Offences, Canada, 2009 and 2010." http://www.statcan.gc.ca/pub/85-002-x/2011001/ article/11523/tbl/tbl04-eng.htm. Statistics on crime in Canada for the years 2009 and 2010.

The National Academies Press. Accessed March 2, 2012. http://www.nap. edu/catalog.php?record_id=12589. A free download of the 350-page 2009 report by the NAS entitled "Strengthening Forensic Science in the United States: A Path Forward" (also available for purchase).

The National Archives. Accessed March 2, 2012. http://webarchive.
nationalarchives.gov.uk/20110218135832/http://rds.homeoffice.gov.uk/rds.
Contains links to crime statistics for England and Wales.

U.S. Geological Survey. Accessed March 2, 2012. http://www.usgs.gov.
Information on soil testing as well as other environment- and Earth-related
topics, such as earthquakes and water issues.

Acknowledgments

Ernie Chaffin, Forensic Chemistry

Dr. Christa Currie, Chemistry

Annette Davis, Serology and DNA

Ed Deters, Death Investigation

Dr. Mark Fischer, Physics

John Heile, Firearms and Toolmarks

Joanna Hughes, Forensic Art

Kathy Isaacs, Research Assistant

Dr. Gene Kritsky, Entomology

Linda Mallory, Courtroom Procedures

Dr. Laureen Marinetti, Toxicology

Colleen McSwiggin, Research Assistant

Suzanne Noffsinger, Hair and Fur

Dr. Bill Ralston, Forensic Pathology

Chief Deputy Mark Whittaker, Law Enforcement

Dr. Frank Wright, Odontology and Forensic Photography